Henry Ritchie

RETURN TO THE PLOUGHSHARE

Dedication

To my farming friends in East Anglia,
My wartime comrades of the Royal Horse Artillery
and for my youngest grand daughter Angelica Charmian Fisher

RETURN TO THE PLOUGHSHARE

By Henry R. Ritchie

From the Burning Sands of Alamein to
the Rolling Acres of East Anglia

First published in Great Britain 1993 by
Marks Hall Publications

ISBN 0 9513164 19

Typeset by Paston Press Ltd, Loddon, Norfolk
Printed and bound by WBC Bookbinders
Bridgend, Mid-Glamorgan

Author's Note

My previous book "The Fusing of the Ploughshare" which became a best seller and ran to four editions took the story of Albert Cooper's war as far as the Battle of Alamein. Amongst the four hundred letters I received after publication some asked what happened after the war to Albert and Julie.

   In "Return to the Ploughshare" I have endeavoured to pick up the thread of the last year of the war and Albert's return to farming in the fields of rural Suffolk.

Henry R. Ritchie
Marks Hall
Margaret Roding
Dunmow
Essex

Acknowledgements

One cannot write a book like this without drawing on the help of a great many people.

My first thanks go to the Hon. G.V.H. Kneale CBE, MA., a wartime comrade and former Minister of Education and Speaker of the House of Keys. Victor Kneale has produced the splendid jacket cover and the superb drawings and illustrations.

A special word of gratitude should go to John Norris CBE, DL., formerly President of the Country Landowners Association, for agreeing to review the book before publication.

My thanks extend to Philip Wrixon, presenter of the BBC Farming Programme, for reading and commenting on the manuscript.

My appreciation and thanks goes to Sir Leonard Crossland, Past Chairman of The Ford Motor Company for his willing support, interest and cooperation.

I welcome the chance to thank Lt. Col. Alan Nicholls CBE, MC. for his time spent in reviewing the book and for his encouragement.

I must record my thanks to Rita Stanley-Smith for her helpful review and for her comments on my work.

Neither must I forget to thank David Short MA, for his help and assistance and also Ray Fullerton and Paul Baker for their help with the early drafts.

Much is owed to Judith Nunn for her patience and her typing and computer expertise.

Most importantly I must specially thank my dear wife who has sustained me from day to day with the same enthusiasm and grace that she has brought to all our ventures together for the last 45 years. This book would not exist without her and neither would I.

Contents

CHAPTER ONE

The Attack

It was the sixteenth day of December 1944. The Second World War was now in its sixth year, and the fighting continued with turbulent fury. Enemy rockets and high explosives, hurled through space, were falling on English cities . . .

*   *   *   *

Fifteen hundred miles to the south-east of Dover and the British coast, His Majesty's troopship *Devonshire*, grey painted, blacked out and heavily laden with time expired men, was under way and heading west. The two thousand men aboard, battle weary and burnt by the sun, were returning from the long, grim Desert War in the Middle East. It was five days since the *Devonshire*, with muted engines, had quietly slipped out of the darkened harbour at Alexandria, past the anchored warships of the British Fleet, and nosed her way into the eastern Mediterranean. The ship was under watchful and vigilant command, the Captain well aware of the dangers from lurking enemy, two-man submarines lying in ambush and the hazards of being exposed to the peril of hostile limpet mines.

The ageing troopship had been hugging the coast of Algeria, leaving in her wake the gallant, much bombed island of Malta and the northern tip of Tunisia. She was now moving at reduced speed, some thirty kilometres to the east of the Rock and would steam with her escorts through the narrow Strait in the gathering darkness. A cold north-easterly was blowing and the weather had worsened. The massive great bulk of the ship sloughed and rocked in the angry green sea.

Among the two thousand returning soldiers aboard the *Devonshire* were one hundred and forty-eight men of my own regiment, the 51st West Suffolk Yeomanry Regiment, Royal Horse Artillery.

In the late evening, as the convoy drew near to the blurred shape of the Rock, the escorting cruisers and destroyers of the Royal Navy moved in closer to the three laden troopships, faintly visible in the dim shadows of the sea.

I had climbed, in almost total darkness, the unsteady gangway from C deck to get some fresh air before turning in for the night. It presented something of a challenge. I had lost a leg on the ninth day of the battle during the break-out from the bridgehead at Alamein. The amputation was below the knee and an artificial leg had been fitted. Although it was fairly comfortable, I still needed crutches. Twice that day I had fallen while trying carefully to pick my way along the wet deck to our cabin. The second fall had resulted in a deep cut over my right eye. I had stuck on a bit of plaster and had not reported sick. I had no wish to return to

the Sick Bay, high in the stern of the ship, where the pitch and roll was at its maximum and left you feeling like a battered shuttlecock. The ship's doctor was probably right to say that I should be in the ship's hospital but since losing my leg I had seen quite enough of doctors, nurses and the inside of military hospitals. Two friends came up to join me on deck. They were Sandy Evans and David Chetwood. Sandy was now Regimental Sergeant-Major and for three years he had been 'A' Troop's Sergeant-Major during the time I had been Gun Sergeant on No 4 gun. We had soldiered together in most of the battles during the war in the desert. Sandy was a soldier in every fibre. He had an ability to command others and a natural authority. He would be getting his commission when we arrived back in England.

My other friend, David Chetwood, was twenty six. He was slightly under average height with a shock of unruly dark brown hair and a neat Errol Flynn moustache. David was a Sergeant in a regiment steeped in history . . . The 11th Hussars. He had won the D.C.M. in 1941, when three armoured cars were out on reconnaisance patrol in the desert area of Southern Libya, and were moving just west of the Jarrubub Oasis. In the shimmering distance of this vast expanse of desert a German reconnaisance force came into view. They were the forward eyes of the German 21st Panzer Division which was lying up in wadis and dried up river beds some forty miles to the north west. The British patrol was in radio contact with a small force of our Long Range Desert Group. The L.R.D.G. were at that time moving some two miles north, parallel to the British Patrol and the 11th Hussars called them over the R.T. Both the British and German detachments were equally surprised at running into an enemy patrol so far south. In the sharp engagement that followed, the British Squadron Commander, his Gunner and his Driver were killed. David, as senior N.C.O. took command and together with the L.R.D.G. and their Besa machine-guns and their 2 pounders, the German motorised column was annihilated, leaving nine enemy dead and three Panzer waggons and one scout car ablaze. The clash of arms was all over in seven minutes. David's armoured car had been hit, he had been badly burnt and to this day bears signs of the skin graft on the left side of his face.

David said, "Albert, you ought to know better than to go traipsing up this gangway on crutches without asking one of us to give you a hand, you'll fall down again and it will serve you bloody well right."

"I can't expect to have a nursemaid with me all the time," I said, "I've got to learn to look after myself and as soon as we reach Blighty I'm going to sling these bloody crutches away."

"If you want to play silly buggers and fall arse over tit, that's up to you," was David's answer.

"You know," said Sandy Evans, lighting up a cigarette, "this time tomorrow we shall be well out into the Atlantic. I shan't be sorry after five years to be saying goodbye to the Med. I've seen enough of this bloody sea and the North African coast. If I've got any more fighting to do in this war, I hope it will be where there are some green fields, a drop or two of running water and a few decent trees around."

"That's what you say now," said David, "but after a couple of days of sleet and fog in Blighty you'll be wishing you were back in the desert again keeping a weather eye out for Stukas and sitting in your gun pit sunning yourself."

"Right now," replied Sandy, "I could put up with twenty years of rain and fog and I shan't cry if I never see a bucket of sand to the end of my days."

The dim dark outline of the Rock of Gibraltar could be discerned as a vast back drop through the last fading minutes of daylight. "This ancient outpost of the British Empire has come in very useful during the last five years," said Sandy, "just as well we didn't give it back to the old matadors and senoritas."

"No doubt it's served its purpose," said David. "Right now though I'd swap Gibraltar for a couple of dusky raven haired senoritas."

The dark ship, with dimmed lights below and blacked-out portholes began to rock and lurch in the busy swell. The wind was rising and the night was chilly. "We'd better get you down below, Albert," said David, catching me by the arm, "before it gets any darker and before you start sliding all over the deck."

*   *   *   *

The sea journey through the Mediterranean had been uneventful, but on the second day out into the Atlantic an enemy, long range Focke-Wulf Condor special reconnaisance aircraft, fitted with extra fuel tanks, appeared and began to shadow the convoy. Through binoculars the black crosses on the fuselage and wings could be clearly seen, as distinct and unmistakeable as when we had watched the German bombers and marauding Messerschmitts flying in to attack us in the desert.

It had been several months since I had seen a German war plane, threatening and hostile, and I felt a shiver of unease and irritation.

The F-W 200 flew leisurely around the convoy, apparently oblivious of the anti-aircraft fire from the Bofors and the Chicago pianos on the escorting warships. Eventually, he turned and flew off to the north east, leaving scores of anti-aircraft puffballs in the disturbed high air above the convoy. It could be safely assumed that information from enemy spies in Gibraltar was bearing fruit.

*   *   *   *

The sailors knew the score and so did we. The wireless operator in the Focke-Wulf would now be transmitting messages, giving our course and speed to the Captains of the U-Boat pack lying out to sea.

The immediate reaction of the convoy Commander was predictable, and the nine ships were ordered to change course and head south west. There were calls from the bridge to the engine room for more revolutions. It was not surprising that the action of the Commander to change course was anticipated by the leader of the U-Boat pack and seven hours later a cluster of hunting U-Boats, programmed to kill, moved in on the convoy. The first signs of the approaching attack came when, over to starboard, one of the escorting destroyers began dropping depth charges. Plumes of water jacketed up to cascade in the evening light, followed seconds later by the deep boom as violent explosions ripped the ocean floor.

H.M.S. Pheasant, one of the 'H' Class escorting destroyers, like a lean grey shark and creating an enormous silvery pluming bow wave, was racing over to starboard at a tremendous rate of knots. H.M.S. Pheasant, built on the Clyde in 1933 and launched by H.M. The Queen, was now on a serious and deadly mission. In this insane moment of truth the lives of thousands of soldiers, sailors and airmen, now in close quarters on the troopships, were in dire peril as the dark sea slid beneath them.

Sandy, David and myself had a grandstand view on C deck, with our life-jackets securely fastened and firmly grasping the slippery handrail. We would not have been human if we had not been filled with apprehension. The three troopships in the middle of the convoy would be the principal targets and in spite of strict censorship it was common knowledge that in that dreadful year of 1941, in one month alone, the U-Boats had sunk no less than one hundred and six British merchantmen and naval ships. In one horrendous action in the Atlantic, a whole convoy had been destroyed with appalling losses of life.

During our years in the desert in our sand-bagged gun pits we had, often enough, been the main targets of an enemy air attack by JU 87's with bombs aboard, spiralling in on us at an angle of 80 degrees. There had been noise and warning before the bombs came torrenting down, but here in the relatively gentle seas of the Atlantic and knowing that under us was a thousand fathoms of water . . . there seemed to be an uncanny, awful death-like silence in the impending ominous menace of the sea.

We were joined by Petty Officer Frank Scobie, a cheerful round-faced, long serving mariner with a grey beard and an impressive beer gut. It was rumoured that Scobie made a thousand pounds a year running the ship's Housey-Housey. Scobie was officially charged with keeping an eye on the Sergeants' welfare.

"Evening, all," called Scobie, jaunty as a cricket.

"Evening, Frank," we replied.

"I expect you lot wish you were somewhere else," said Petty Officer Scobie.

"We did not get on this boat to be torpedoed," I said, "we loaded ourselves on this bloody troopship of yours to take us back to Blighty."

"Not to worry," was Scobie's ready advice, with his eyes set firmly on the two destroyers deployed out to starboard and still looking full of business. "I should estimate that the chances of this boat getting a torpedo in its guts are not less than ten to one and I can also inform you that since you squaddies sailed through the Med. to Haifa in 1939, the Navy's counter measures have considerably changed for the better and the new anti-submarine tactics have improved out of all recognition."

"No doubt the U-Boat Commanders have also learnt a thing or two since 1939," said David, looking thoughtful.

"How many U-Boats do you think there are out there, Frank?" enquired Sandy.

"Sometimes, in the North Atlantic," said Scobie, who was well-versed in these affairs, "there have been as many as twenty U-Boats in a pack, but I very much doubt if there are more than two or three down as far south as this. They are probably," he went on, "all U-Boat type VII's, and although they are fairly fast on the surface and can keep up with the convoys, they can only do about eight knots under the water and the convoys can leave the subs well behind. "Sometimes," said Scobie, still with his eyes glued on the two destroyers, "really experienced U-Boat Commanders will get right inside our screen and they have been known to get close enough to a ship to fire their torpedoes from as little as three hundred yards. Other times they will do a bit of fish tailing right in the middle of the convoy."

There was another series of muffled explosions as one of the destroyers pumped out a pattern of depth charges and the surface of the sea boiled. "The cunning bastards may be trying to lure the escorts away from the troopships," said Scobie.

We knew that Scobie was lucky to be alive as, on one of the Russian Convoys, he had been on the merchantman the *Glencomer* when she was sunk off Iceland in the winter of 1941. Scobie had been on a life-raft for six hours, in the bitter cold, before being picked up. They had been the longest six hours of his life, and three of his comrades were already dead from exposure when the raft was found, just as the northern darkness was closing in.

"How many torpedoes does the type VII carry?" I asked.

"Well," said Scobie, pulling his duffle coat collar up round his neck, "the standard type carries fourteen torpedoes altogether. The fish are twenty five feet long and twenty one inches in diameter. Four sit in the fixed launching tubes for'ard and there is another one ready to fire in the aft tube. When these have been fired the tubes can be re-loaded from inside the hull."

"Let's hope then that the sub isn't pointing its snout in this direction," said David, meaningfully.

"It doesn't have to be spot on," said Scobie, "They now have acoustic torpedoes that automatically home in on the noise of the ship's propeller."

"You're a cheerful bugger," said Sandy, "I thought that as long as there's enough daylight you can see the torpedo heading towards you and take evasive action. They tell me you can see the track of the air bubbles."

"You're four years out of date," said Scobie. "As you seem to have heard, the torpedoes used to be driven by compressed air, but now they are fitted with electric engines, powered by lead storage batteries, so, no bubbles."

"I think, Frank," said Sandy, "that you had better pipe down, you don't leave anything to the imagination."

*   *   *   *

Then suddenly, like a shock wave smashing into our senses, it happened. The troopship *Huntingdon Castle*, converted from a P&O luxury liner into a troop carrying vessel in 1940, was outlined in the semi-darkness. She was moving a thousand yards away and parallel to us on the port side. Like hell run wild, the *Huntingdon Castle* was struck amidships. There was an enormous flash, like a serpent's tongue and one – two – three loud detonations which rocketed across the dark sea. A colossal pillar of flame billowed upwards, a mammoth geyser of fire creating sheets of flame in its molten furnace and laying a flaming carpet on the waves of the sea. A killer submarine had slipped inside the screen. There followed another quieter explosion and the flame broke slowly into the sky like a spreading crimson petal.

One of the torpedoes had exploded in the engine room and the great ship appeared to hesitate, lose impetus and then ceased forward movement. She shuddered herself to a standstill like the final moments of a mortally wounded, harpooned, whale – frigid and bleak and stiffened with disaster.

We watched in horror as the bow of the *Huntingdon Castle* began to rise little by little, like a black accusing monument, high out of the writhing waters dragging its slow forward bulk towards the sky. The great, doomed ship was faltering in its helpless agony and suspending that awful, final, smouldering moment. Doomed men could be seen jumping off the bow, they had no chance. For ten long seconds the stricken troopship seemed to stand on its very end. With flame and smoke cascading, as a monstrous gushing volcano, she steadied for one dreadful moment of horror, poised for the long slide, before slithering like the hand of a drowning giant, slowly, slowly into the cloying caverns of the sea. With a great upheaval of seething air bubbles the sea boiled in its torment.

"Christ," said Scobie, who over the last three bitter years on Atlantic convoys had seen merchantmen and oilers and fighting ships sent to the bottom, "I've never seen a ship go down in such a bloody hurry."

The Captain of the Huntingdon Castle, forty eight members of the crew, eight hundred and thirty two soldiers and fourteen young girls, members of the Women's Auxiliary Air Force, were sent to their last account in this outrageous collision with violence. The soldiers from famous regiments of the line were saturated with service and warfare and had been homeward bound after long years of duty in remote foreign stations. In this savage destruction of life, soldiers,

V. Kneale.

sailors and airmen, with sweethearts, wives and children at home, were dragged down into the hollow depths of the ocean by the terrible merciless suction. There would be no survivors and we shuddered in the damp cold with shock and fear. The two destroyers, *Pheasant* and *Auckland* turned towards us at speed and began to circle the two remaining troopships in a clockwise direction at a radius of fifteen hundred metres. The *Pheasant* threw another pattern of depth charges and hammer-cracking explosions rent the heavy dusk of the evening. The night, driven by the north east wind, turned colder and there seemed to be a foul unpleasant odour manifest from the sea.

"We shall be all right now," said Scobie, "I can't see a U-Boat hanging around here for many minutes and I shouldn't want to be the Commander of that U-Boat out there. These destroyers have got enough equipment to find the bastard sub and to blow it to bits."

Scobie was trying to cheer us up but in these awful moments, full of horror and sick at heart, we had been too close to death. We had watched, transfixed and full of dread, that livid, final flame and this great obscene drowning of the sea.

* * * *

Petty Officer Scobie proved to be right and after the convoy had taken a ten degree turn to starboard and picked up speed the U-Boats lost contact. None of the escorts stopped to look for survivors. No Captain could expose his ship to this crucible of danger in these hazardous waters.

Back in the cabin we felt more claustrophobic than ever, Sandy Evans said, "I've seen some slaughter in my time and I've seen the dead piled up in the trenches and gunpits at Alamein, but never anything like this."

David said, "I reckon we could all do with a treble malt," and he moved over to his well stocked locker.

CHAPTER TWO
We Join an Eastbound Convoy

It had been five years since I had put my feet up against the Rayburn in the kitchen of my mother's thatched cottage and had wakened to a day of peace and to the soft lowing of the cattle in the water meadows behind the garden fence; five years since I had kissed my golden haired sweetheart, Julie, goodbye in the final moments of my embarkation leave in 1939. Julie, wearing my engagement ring, was just seventeen when I had left her. She had written me two letters every week and all that time I had wanted to be with her. She had told me in her earlier letters when I went overseas that her only relief were tears and sleep. I had ached for her voice and the touch of her fingers in a darkened room. A balance had been found and a balance broken. There would surely be a renewal of our love, unmolested by fear and the bitterness of war.

I had thought of returning to England and of Julie and I having a cottage of our own in a Suffolk village . . . it was a dream born in the blaze of the sun. Set against that burning fire of hope and mystery was that black sheet of ice, that wall of arrogant terror – the German Nation. With enemy U-boat packs out there in the grey sea, I dismissed from my mind the possible ruined remnants and candle ends of my existence. The horror of the day had lent a sharp edge to my determined desire for life and survival.

*   *   *   *

During the night the convoy changed course and headed north west towards the coast of Nova Scotia and two days later at some dark rendezvous, in the boundless sweep of the sea, the convoy Commander made contact with a mighty armada of ships sailing towards Europe from the United States of America and Canada. The ships were laden with oil and food and weapons of war. Tanks and guns could be discerned roped on to the decks. The convoy changed direction and we turned towards the east. Sailing in the middle of this great fleet of American liberty ships, with the east wind blowing into our faces, it put the edge on our reassurance that at long last we were homeward bound.

On the second day of our journey eastwards a mighty ocean liner could be seen out to starboard. She was ploughing her way majestically parallel to us, but outside the convoy. "That," said Petty Officer Scobie, looking through his binoculars, "is the *Queen Mary*, she goes like the clappers and will soon be leaving us far behind. She'll do thirty-five knots and she's so fast that she doesn't need an escort." Then he went on, "in any case, none of the escorts could keep up with her.

As you'll probably remember," said Scobie, "that ship was launched at Clydebank in September 1934, she's the world's first 1000 ft. liner and her gross weight is 81,000 tons."

"Surely she's vulnerable to a U-Boat attack," I asked.

"No, not really," Scobie told us, "By zigzagging at speed, it is almost impossible for a U-Boat to get into a position where they are able to fire torpedoes with any accuracy. Both the *Queens* have been fitted out as troopships and as you will know, they brought most of the Aussies out to you in the Middle East. They now spend most of their time ferrying American troops over to Europe."

It was two days before Christmas 1944 and those of us who had served on the guns with the West Suffolk Yeomanry were about to spend our sixth Christmas away from home. However, we felt much more secure in this massive convoy of fifty seven England bound ships. The convoy was escorted by an aircraft carrier, two cruisers and five destroyers of the British Fleet. In the daylight hours a four-engined Shackleton, with anti-submarine equipment, flew overhead like a hovering shepherd of the sky.

*   *   *   *

During the late evening of the second day, heading east, there was a distinct sharpening of the weather. The winds strengthened and rolling waves smashed against the beam of The *Devonshire*. Unlike many of the accredited and hardened seamen aboard, we had not experienced the merciless power of the waves in a rough North Atlantic running sea in the depths of winter. The forecast was for the weather to worsen and by the following morning the winds had whipped up to gale force. The *Devonshire*, with her heavy burden of war weary troops, shook and rattled in the buffeting swell of ice cold waves. At eleven o'clock in the morning there was one violent forty degree roll as the troopship plunged into a mountainous head sea. This was closely followed by a shuddering crunch and the noisy slamming of cabin doors. There was water, water everywhere. In the late afternoon, with the dusk closing in, the wind veered to the north. The freezing waters hurled themselves across the heaving ocean.

Clouds stretched in a solid grey mass as they rolled across the black sky. The lash of heavy rain beat through the waves of thunder. The vicious winter gale was at its zenith. Throughout the night the wind howled around us as the storm thrashed out its fury.

Sandy and David had wedged me tightly into my berth in the cabin to ride out the storm. The sea sickness was exhausting. It was difficult to stay unhurt and to avoid being thrown out of our bunks. We were buffeted and bruised as tons of green sea and sheets of rain raged against the solid dimensions of the troopship. During the afternoon, from the top of a huge freak wave, the ship was flung into the very pit and abyss of the wild ocean. It was as if a mountain was sliding down the very surface of the earth. "One thing," shouted Sandy above the storm, as we braced ourselves for another big dipper into the caverns of the sea, "the bloody U-Boats won't molest us in this weather." Sandy was hanging on to the wall-rail by his bunk, and was the only one amongst us who was not laid low with appalling sea sickness. As he spoke a violent lurch broke his grip and threw him against the cabin locker.

"I hope," said David from the depths of his blankets, "that a bloody great torpedo explodes right under my sodding bunk and puts me out of my misery. I've never felt so rough in all my life."

Throughout the afternoon and evening the wild abrasive wind raged on, lashing the dark clouds down into the far horizon. There was an awful stench of vomit. All the portholes were blacked over and never opened. The black-out was absolute. In the half dark, loose objects went crashing everywhere, sleep was impossible. The sky was jet black and for two long days we were at the mercy of the waves and captives of the storm.

On the morning of the third day the angry winds dropped and beams of sunlight were getting to work on the water. Spears of golden light splashed across the heavens. A new, soft, fresh breeze blew through the cabin door. We were conscious of an immense relief, it was like a new world of soft light and warmth as the driven waves settled and the *Devonshire*, pushing her sharp edged bows and `driving forward through the sea, steamed eastwards, like a river swan, on an even keel.

CHAPTER THREE

The Return

On the morning of the fifth day, after joining the eastbound convoy, the leading destroyer slid into the broad mouth of the Mersey. It was just after midday when Sandy, who was up on deck, shouted down to us. "I can see the tower. I can see the bloody tower!"

"Come on, Albert," said David, handing me my crutch, "and take a shufti at your first sight of Blighty for five years. Better let me give you a hand up the gangway."

"No thanks," I said, "I don't intend to use these bloody crutches anymore, I can manage O.K."

And so it was on this murky English day, a few days after Christmas 1944, the storm-battered *Devonshire* slipped into her berth in the Liverpool Docks, with cheers of joy and happiness rising from the packed decks. Gas filled barrage balloons floated above the still grey sea. A 'Z' class Corvette, now gently rolling in the rocking waves, lay three hundred yards to starboard, its own barrage balloon aloft like a weightless denizen of the air, bound and secured to long mooring cables.

As we sailed into the river it became clear that there had been a massive enemy air raid on Liverpool. The docks had been hit in a dozen places. Two enormous warehouses had been gutted and burned to cinders. Behind two twisted cranes there were ugly gaps like a giant's missing teeth in the rows of terraced houses.

Bombadier Eric Wilkinson, a line signaller in 'B' Troop, caught me by the arm and said, "You know, Albert, we weren't told anything about this. We had heard all about the raid on Coventry when the Cathedral had been destroyed, but they have tried to keep quiet on the Liverpool bombing. There must have been scores of people killed here in those terraced houses."

"Know anyone in Liverpool?" I asked.

"My eldest sister, Betty, and my brother-in-law, Bill, lived there in Shaws Alley before the War," said Bombadier Wilkinson. "Shaws Alley is only a few yards from Salthouse Docks. Bill joined the Navy and he was killed when the cruiser *Birmingham* was sunk by dive bombers on one of the Russian convoy runs. It happened just off Spitzbergen in the Barents Sea. My sister then went to St. Helens to live with my mother. I was best man at Bill and Betty's wedding, while on embarkation leave in 1939."

"There's hardly a family in Britain," I said, "that hasn't been touched by the loss of a relative during this war."

*   *   *   *

Later in the morning what was officially known as 'disembarkation' commenced and we moved step by step down the heaving gangway. Our back packs and haversacks were crammed with souvenirs and presents from the milling casbahs and suks of Egypt, Palestine and Syria. The sun was trying to shine and down on the wet quay, at the bottom of our gangway, a military band struck up a cheerful score of martial music. "It's certainly pleasing to be welcomed home by a full strength military band," said Lance Bombadier Cookson of the 107th Regiment R.H.A., "and when have I heard that tune before?"

"You should certainly recognise that tune," said a Lieutenant of the Northumberland Fusiliers. "That band down there is the American Air Force Band and it's playing the *Star Spangled Banner*, and I reckon they're perched on the wrong bit of concrete." As he spoke the blue uniformed members of the band stopped playing, picked up their instruments and marched along to the next ship where hundreds of G.I.s were filing down the gangway.

There was no welcoming band for us and we watched, with envious eyes, the two pretty girls handing out chocolate and cigarettes to the American soldiers. The Americans were making their first contact with England and were on their way to join their comrades in Europe.

We were returning home to a war weary England, weary of the shortages and the rationing and the bombing. The Country and its people were exhausted and jaded from the years of standing alone against the mighty German war machine – the most powerful military force the world had ever known. Behind us now lay the war torn years in the desert. They had been hard years. It had been a world without women, a world without softness. We had been roughened by the war and the harsh layers of tension in the desert battlefields. In the burning heat and the choking dust we had longed to sit with our feet sprawled before an English winter fire, with perhaps a tumbler of chilled beer beside us and a sleep from which there was a quiet awakening. We felt that we had experienced every sensation and that we had seen it all . . . and now we longed for home.

At the same time as I was working my way down the gangway of the *Devonshire* three farm workers, Steve King, Doddy Hayes and Sweedy Baxter were riddling potatoes in a big old thatched barn in West Suffolk. They were all in their late fifties and as they were farm workers were excused military service. I had known them all before the war in Newton Green, in fact, I had been at the village school with Steve's son, Will, who was killed while flying a glider at Arnhem, and Doddy had taught me how to use a scythe and how to sharpen the blade on the whetstone.

Because of the war it was only a three-quarter gang. Steve was forking the potatoes off the pile on to the shaking sieves on the riddle. Doddy was turning the handle and Sweedy was bagging up the potatoes at the delivery end and tying the tops with string.

They had run out of empty bags and there was a pause in their work while Sweedy went along to the other end of the barn to fetch half a dozen replacements. There was an opportunity for a few minutes breather and Steve propped his fork up against the riddle and lit up the half Woodbine which had remained unlit in his mouth for the past half hour and now was thoroughly wet at one end. Doddy picked up the oil can and gave a couple of squirts on the driving cogs of the riddle. There had been a hell of a how-d'ye-do the day before. A German Junkers 88 bomber, fully loaded had set out from an airfield near the German coast to bomb Ipswich. They had dropped their bombs well wide of the mark when a patrolling Spitfire appeared out of the clouds and shot the Junkers down. However, the enemy pilot had managed to land the plane in a thirty acre field in Haselbury Parva, the village right next door to Newton Green. There had been four men aboard the bomber and they had come out with their hands up and had been taken prisoner by soldiers from the Ack-Ack unit which was in position in the vicinity.

"If Oi'd bin there," said Doddy, "Oi'd hev run they owd Garmins fru wiv moi four toined fork."

"Yew couldn't hev done 'em in all at once," said Steve, "yew couldn't hev got a Garmin on each toine."

"Oi'd hev giv 'em wot for," said Doddy, placing the oil can firmly back on the bale of straw.

"They reckon," said Sweedy, "that owd Hitler was in that airy plane."

Sweedy knew that was true because his cousin, Sid, who was in the Home Guard had been sent up with five others to guard the plane. Although Sid had not arrived on the scene until an hour after the crew had been marched off he heard that one of the crew looked exactly like Hitler.

Sid had told Sweedy that Hitler had said to Luther Owen, who was doing a bit of hedging and ditching near where the plane landed, that he was glad to be in England as he was fed up with being in Berlin with the R.A.F. bombing him every night. It was not clear whether Hitler spoke English or Luther spoke German, but the tale certainly caught on.

By the time the story had had another twenty four hours to cook round the area not only was Hitler aboard but also his mistress, Eva Braun. As it appeared that four men had come out of the aircraft it was clear to everyone that Eva was disguised as a man and, as far as Newton Green was concerned the capture of Hitler and Eva Braun meant that the war was as good as over.

Sweedy cleared the small heap of dirt which had accumulated under the riddle and hooked another empty bag on the riddle.

*   *   *   *

By the end of 1944 the British and American armies were advancing deep into Europe and the German armies were in retreat. However, the German military machine was still threatening and highly dangerous with its new high technology weaponery, rockets and missiles. The vicious desperate counter attacks by German tank divisions in the Ardennes were as the convolutions of a dying cobra in its death agonies.

*   *   *   *

Our long column of disembarked soldiery was marshalled to the railway station where we climbed aboard a dirty, dingy, unswept and unheated train. The smoky carriages and the drab worn seats were stained and musty from neglect and dross of the years of war.

Our destination was to be the barracks at Woolwich in London where we were to be processed back into the Home Army establishment. Our webbing back packs and our haversacks were slung onto the luggage racks. There were some of the West Suffolk Yeomanry soldiers amongst us, back from the eastern sun, who were now fraught with apprehension at the prospect of homecoming. Some would have heard rumours of wifely infidelity and there might be old scores to settle. There were five year olds at home who had never seen their fathers. There were American Air Force bases in Suffolk.

*   *   *   *

I will never forget that train journey down to London. We had just taken course from a burnt, treeless land of sand and arid harshness. Now we gazed out of dirty carriage windows at the tiny green fields and orchards and neat winter gardens. There were well-kept pastures and green winter meadows with grey-faced North Country sheep grazing alongside placid dairy cows. The softness soothed our eyes and calmed our minds. We passed dairy herds of brown and white, big bodied Ayrshires with their long, graceful horns and well-shaped udders. There were Roan dairy Shorthorns, which for many long years had been the dominant breed in the milking herds of Britain but were now being replaced by the black and white Friesians with their great capacity not only to provide vast quantities of milk but also to supply the major share of the British beef market.

We were riveted in wonder as we gazed on lush meadows, wet leaves and dripping trees. There were smoke-coloured, back to back, houses, coal sheds and laden washing lines. Above us hung a web of low cloud. It wasn't much of a drying day.

An hour and a half later, the train, after what seemed to be an unnecessary and exasperating chuntering of buffers and the release of high pressure steam, came to a jerky halt at Platform 3 at Crewe. Information was relayed down the train that there would be a twenty minute halt and there would be time to get a cup of tea at the station buffet. David and I joined the forty yard long queue and when we at last drew in somewhere near the wet, tea-stained counter the canteen smelt of wet uniforms, stale tobacco and weak ersatz coffee. There was nowhere to sit. There was very little milk and no sugar. The butterless cheese rolls were as dry as a bag of chaff. We were experiencing some of the miseries of war-time England. Our twenty minute stop lasted two hours and ten minutes and it was late evening, after nine dreary hours on the train, when we reached our destination. We were tired from the journey and stiff and sore with aching limbs. Everyone was surly on discipline.

After leaving the station we marched up the hill in very ragged formation and soon we entered the gates of the British Army's historic and infamous Royal Artillery Barracks at Woolwich. The huge, plain garrison buildings stood out as a bleak, cold and cheerless edifice of brick and concrete. We had reached that fender and stronghold of the Royal Artillery, where guns and toecaps had been burnished by many generations. This ancient military monument in south east London, where over the long years Gunners had been assigned with their pack batteries and their screw guns to India, Aden and the North West Frontier. Artillery men had been drafted from Woolwich to China, Egypt and to the Sudan and many foreign stations in the East, where the steaming heat was a torment and mauled the senses. Here the old sweats spoke of dark-eyed natives with knives for slitting the throats of the white infidels and the hated white oppressors. They spoke of defaulters and captives tied to the wheel of a gun carriage in the heat of the midday sun. They told of places where the Empire glowed and dark-skinned lives were cheap and of garrison towns where troops were cavalier and contemptuous of the natives. Others boasted of the sensual and responsive black and brown bints with whom they had slept in the dimly lit brothels of the East.

The Sergeants' accommodation at Woolwich was quite tolerable, but the junior N.C.O.'s and the Gunners were directed to sleep on tiered bunks in the stables, where horses that drew the guns and limbers had lived and slept and were cosseted and pampered. In the days of the horse, the young Subalterns were left in no doubt by their senior officers that the correct order of priorities was horses, men, officers. Every soldier knew, of course, that the practical interpretation of this friendly declaration was, officers first, horses second and lastly the men. Woe betide any trooper of the R.H.A. who had fed himself before his horse had been groomed, fed and watered. The men polished and burnished and sweated over bits and leathers in the horse lines. In winter they were up at six o'clock to break the ice in the water troughs and do 'stables'. It fell to the troopers to pick up in their bare hands the round balls of dung lying in the heans of the well-forked bedding of oat straw.

*   *   *   *

It was a cold, clear, December night and the London sky was overspread by myriads of stars. I had telephoned Mr Jessop, my father's employer, to ask him to let my parents know that I was well, that I had arrived back in England, and that I would be arriving at Middlesham Station at around eleven o'clock on the following morning. The busy day of travel was now drawing to its close, and late that winter's evening, Sandy, David and I were in the Sergeants' Mess, seated round a small, green-painted table, consuming pints of old English beer as if we had just come off the desert. In the centre of our table was a cut-down, brass charge case from a twenty-five pounder gun. It was now nearly full of butt ends and half-smoked cigarettes. The air in the mess was curdled with a beery fug. A young, bespectacled, fair-haired sergeant from the Pay Corps was strumming something slow and mournful from Cole Porter on the beer-stained piano. We were in a mood of detached intoxication.

There were old soldiers there who were hardened drinkers and that no-one could drink under the table. There were 'ten pint' men who after a full evening drinking and, although their eyes were bloodshot and bleary, would get up and walk to their quarters as steady as a standard bearer of the British Legion.

It was just after eleven o'clock, the pianist was suffering from too much free beer, and was slumped with his head on the lid of the piano. The returned glasses were being dipped hurriedly into the beery water which sloshed in the tin bucket standing on an empty crate under the bar. A dirty grey cloth, saturated and ale-soaked, lay inert on the end of the wet bar, like a dead rat.

Suddenly, without any warning, there was a tremendous explosion. The sixty watt bulb in the middle of the Mess ceiling trembled like a tuning fork. The windows and the glasses on the shelves behind the bar rattled and clinked and the canteen door blew open. "Christ," said Sandy, "what the hell was that?"

"That, " said Sergeant Edwards of the Base Depot, who was sitting in one of the easy chairs and reading a well-thumbed edition of *Picture Post*, "was a V2 Rocket which probably landed half a mile away. During the past few weeks we've been getting about fifteen a day on London. They will flatten nearly everything within a quarter of a mile."

"Good Lord," said Sandy, "where the hell do they come from?"

"The V2s are launched from the German coast and are shot out of the rocket launchers where they are propelled to a height of some sixty miles before coming down on London. The warhead weighs a ton. I expect," said Sergeant Edwards, who had hardly raised his head from his magazine, "that you did not come across too many V2 Rockets in the desert?" Sergeant Edwards, who had spent the whole of the War at Woolwich Base Depot, was acutely aware that we were wearing the Africa Star Ribbon and had just returned from five years overseas. He was probably a little envious and perhaps felt slightly guilty at having a London-based job, but it was clear that there was certainly no guarantee that a 'base' job at Woolwich would give anyone an assurance of eternal life.

CHAPTER FOUR
Blighty

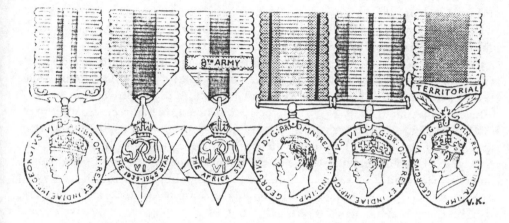

The next morning, after a hurried breakfast in the Sergeants' mess of dried egg powder, mixed to the consistency of custard and fried bread, I dumped my blue canvas kit bag in the back of the 8cwt duty truck which was standing outside the Battery Office. I had drawn my free travel pass from the Battery Office and slinging my kitbag over my shoulder I climbed into the truck beside the driver, Lance Bombadier Leslie Watkins.

"Morning, Sarge," he said, "I believe I'm to take you to Liverpool Street."

"That's right," I said.

"Hope the station is still there," said Lance Bombadier Watkins, "there was a heavy raid in the East End last night."

* * * *

At Liverpool Street Station, the London terminal for all the North Eastern lines, I stood looking up at the great indicator board listing train arrivals and departures. Then, throwing my kit bag over my shoulder, I made my way over to the number eleven platform. Over an hour later the old wartime steam engine, built in 1908, chuntered into the grubby station three quarters of an hour late. There was a rush for seats as the carriages filled with soldiers on leave, drab civilians and crying children.

Standing there in the cramped and smoke-filled, narrow corridor, with its steaming windows and uncomfortable mass of grey humanity, I was filled yet again with foolish irrational fears and apprehensions. I knew my mother and father would give me a glowing, warm-hearted welcome and they would probably be proud of me and relieved that I was home, but what of Julie? I had loved her and left her five years ago. Would the same loving Julie be waiting for me? Would my hard, uncouth existence in the wartime desert have roughened my very character and changed me for the worse? Did I care anymore?

In the battle areas we had fought and lived in comradeship in an uncertain hammering danger and priorities were clear. There are less niceties of behaviour when survival is paramount. How much time would I need to adjust to new values and new pressures? I fretted and worried.

I changed trains at Shenfield. A number of soldiers remained on the train to join their regiment at Colchester Barracks prior to their return to France.

Just after half-past eleven the train rumbled, with a protracted noisy clatter and hissing of steam and came to a halt at the station platform at Middlesham. The station had hardly changed since the day I left to join my regiment for overseas duties in Palestine in 1939. No part of the station structure had received a scrap of paint. The same two old red buckets, one filled with water and the other with sand, still hung outside the dreary, unheated, waiting room. I pushed open the carriage door and dropped my kit bag onto the platform, and before I could climb down my hand had been seized and shaken by George Buckle, who had worked at the station since he left school and was now the Station Master. He stood there with his bushy moustache, wearing his old blue peaked cap and well-worn uniform with its dull red piping. George said, "Welcome home, Albert, I got wind that you were going to be on this train and I thought I'd be the first to shake you by the hand."

"I didn't expect to get a welcome from the Station Master himself," I said.

"Sorry I haven't got any flags to put up for you," said George. "Your parents are up by the ticket office. I'll give you a hand with your kit bag."

My mother and father were standing at the top of the stairs. Dad was in his best suit and Mum was wearing a cheap fur coat against the cold. Dad held out his hand and said, "Welcome home, son. This is one of the happiest days of my life." It wasn't like Dad to say that and my heart ran high. My mother let go of Dad's arm and flung herself into my arms and when I kissed her there was no stemming her tears of joy.

"Oh, Albert," she said, touching the three stripes on my sleeve, "we are so proud of you."

I was still blackened and burnt by the sun and several people on the station were looking at my Military Medal ribbon and the Africa Star with the Eighth Army clasp.

Very few soldiers had, as yet, returned home from the Middle East, and I was obviously a matter of some attention and curiosity. A tall, silver-haired, distinguished looking civilian in his city suit looked at my ribbons and said, "I wonder if I could buy you and your mother and father a drink?"

"We'd better get back," said my mother.

"It won't take long, Mum," I said and turning to the tall gentleman I said, "thank you very much, sir. I am sure that we should like to join you." We followed him into the Saloon Bar of the 'Horse and Groom' in Station Road, with its low ceiling and yellow-painted walls and its stale smoky haze.

"What are you going to drink?" our host asked.

I said, "I expect, Mum, that you still go in for a port and lemon?"

"That will do nicely, thank you, sir," said my mother.

"And Dad, I expect you'll have a pint of Adnams?" I said, knowing that this was the local brew.

"I've never said 'no' to a pint of Adnams," said my father, "even if it is a cold morning."

My mother and father took a seat on one of the wooden benches against the wall facing the Bar and I picked my pint off the counter and the gentleman ordered a pink gin, which put him, as far as I was concerned, straight into the Officer Class. I couldn't ever remember anyone ordering a pink gin in the Sergeants' Mess. "You may find the wartime beer a bit on the weak side," he said.

"That won't worry me," I said, "this is the first pint I've had in an English pub for over five years. Good luck, sir," I said as I raised my glass.

"Good luck, Sergeant," he said "and welcome home. My name's Marchbank and the reason I have asked you to come and have a drink with me is that I noticed your Africa Star and the Eighth Army clasp, and I thought you might have been at Alamein."

"All nine days of it," I told him.

"Well, both my sons were killed at Alamein. They were both commissioned in 1942. Geoffrey was a Squadron Commander with Sherman Tanks and was operating with the 10th Armoured Division when his tank was hit on the fifth day of the battle, and Andrew, the younger brother, was killed two days later when leading a platoon attack on a German machine gun position on the Ruweisat Ridge."

"I am sorry," I said, remembering the sickening carnage and the loss of loyal comrades in the cauldron of that fierce relentless battle, when every yard of ground had been bitterly fought for.

"They are now both in the British cemetery at Alamein and I shall go out there when the War is over."

Although it was more than a year since the Battle of Alamein, my mind churned as the memories flooded back into my sub-concious.

"Albert lost a leg at Alamein," volunteered my father.

"I didn't realise," said Marchbank, "I am so sorry. What happened?"

"Stood too close to a 105mm shell," I said.

"Above or below the knee?"

"Below the knee," I said, "and the tin leg is fairly comfortable. Could have been a lot worse."

"What is more," said my mother, "Albert didn't have to go. He worked on the land, you see."

"Oh, shut up, Mum," I said, "I volunteered and that's that."

Our host then said, "Here's my card," and he handed me a small printed card which read . . .

Lord Peregrine Marchbank, P.C., D.S.O., M.C.,
Stanway Castle
Northamptonshire.

"If you are ever up in Northhamptonshire," he said, "do call in, my wife and I would be delighted to show you round the Castle and the estate. I'm afraid we had to plough up over one hundred acres of the park, which has rather spoilt the view from the Castle, but we managed to take off two useful crops of winter wheat in 1942 and 1943."

*   *   *   *

"I'm sure that he was a very brave man in the 1914 War," my mother said as the taxi took us home.

"Well, he wouldn't have got the D.S.O and the Military Cross for feeding the regimental goat," I said.

"Wasn't it Lord Marchbank who gave the Government enough money to build two Spitfires?" said my mother.

"Could have been," said my father, " I shouldn't have thought he is short of a bob or two."

*   *   *   *

It was now thawing and the trees were running with water and the snow was dripping off the rooftops and when we came onto my father's cottage with its thatched roof and its black weather-boarding my mind was stretched and my senses were churning. I heard the familiar sound of the click on the garden gate. My mother led the way up the old brick path and then under the eaves of the cottage, carrying my haversack and pack, and Dad bringing up the rear with my kit bag.

I was still trying to set my mind to the unaccustomed sound of a female voice when my mother said, "There's a surprise for you indoors. Your young lady has been here since eight o'clock."

"Julie. Julie." I caught my breath, my mind was in a whirl and my heart was beating like a drum. My mother lifted the latch on the back door and I stepped onto the multi-coloured rag rug.

"She's in the front room," said my mother, "The fire's lit."

Julie was standing in the far corner of the room and she rushed towards me and we folded into each other's arms.

"Julie. *Julie*," I cried, as I held her to me. Her eyes were wet with tears and the warm scent of her hair was close to my cheek and my heart was on fire.

I kissed her and she said, "Darling Albert, you are never to leave me again."

"Let me look at you," I said, brushing back her hair and I saw the pretty set of her shoulders, her loveliness and her happiness. Her golden hair glistened in the faint afternoon sunlight which streamed through the small lattice window and caught the splashes of gold. I was aware of the soft touch of her fingers. I was breathing light and I knew that I loved her more than anything on earth.

Dad and Mum, one way and another, had been creating a great deal of noise and clatter. There had been a lot of coughing, moving around of chairs, laying of plates, cups and cutlery on the table and much stomping round the kitchen. After about ten minutes Dad shouted, "Are you two going to stay in there all day? I'm just going to open a bottle." Dad still worked for Mr. Jessop at Newton Manor who had somehow found a bottle of champagne, which he had told Dad was to be opened on my return.

Julie and I came back into the kitchen, arm in arm, and Dad was easing out the cork with his thumbs. Four unmatched glasses stood on the scrubbed wooden table. In the softness and warmth of the cottage everything seemed so full of peace. All four of us were brimmed with happiness as the red firelight spread on the brick floor in the scarlet glow of the kitchen.

"We mustn't get tiddly," said my mother, handing Julie champagne in the best of the four glasses.

"Why not?" said my father, "If we can't get tiddly when Albert comes home after five years away, I don't know when we can." My father raised his glass and said, "Welcome home, Albert."

I was still only just coming to grips with the fantasy of it all and my mind was still floating. It had only been forty eight hours since the *Devonshire*, with two thousand troops aboard, had been almost standing on its nose in the teeth of a North Atlantic gale and only six short days since I had witnessed the horrific sinking of the troopship the *Huntingdon Castle* in the savage waters of the wild Atlantic.

Julie squeezed my arm. We were enfolded in a cushion of delight and in these moments of magic Julie seemed to fill the room with a glow of secret happiness.

CHAPTER FIVE

The Dance

The next day was a Saturday and Julie and I had been invited to the Middlesham Young Farmers' Dance, to be held at the Lower Moreton Village Hall about one and a half miles away.

During the afternoon we were over with Julie's parents on their smallholding at Newton Green and I said, "You know I can't dance with this leg."

Julie said, "Of course you can. I'll look after you."

"And what is more," I went on, "I'm going to wear civvies."

"Oh no you're not," said Julie firmly. "You are going in your uniform. I want to show you off."

Julie stood there smiling and she came across and gave me a little kiss. "Just this once," she said.

"Julie," I said, "I will have you know that I am a Gun Sergeant and I'm not used to being given orders from an unimportant little whippersnapper like you!"

*   *   *   *

Petrol was strictly rationed and car journeys for social visits were virtually forbidden while the war was on, so Julie and I biked over to Lower Moreton. We arrived at the Village Hall at around eight o'clock and leaned our bikes against the chestnut paling fence, which had recently been erected to keep Sid Mott's cows from rubbing themselves on the grey-painted weatherboard walls.

Most of the Young Farmers had travelled to the Dance on their bikes but two of them had arrived on tractors. Dermott Scully had turned up in his green painted, three ton Bedford lorry, with a cross bred Friesian bull calf in the back. If the Police came round to check if petrol was being used illegally then Dermott would have to spin a yarn about being on his way to deliver the calf to a neighbour.

The inside of the Hall was cheerful, in spite of only being illuminated by oil lamps. The Christmas paper decorations, made by the village children for their Christmas party, were still in place and the heavy black-out curtains were tightly drawn.

I had been determined not to limp and when Julie and I stepped into the Hall, Bob Sellens, the Club President, came over and shook me warmly by the hand. Bob was a good-hearted, ruddy faced dairy farmer, whose Scottish ancestry had led him into owning a splendid pedigree herd of Ayrshire cattle. Two months earlier he had been up to Scotland to see the Bargower Herd, the Holy Grail of the Ayrshire world, and purchased a bull, with milk in its pedigree, for several thousand pounds.

Bob said, "I heard that you were back, Albert. It *is* good to see you, how long have you been home?"

"Only a couple of days," I said.

"You must have been away for five years," said Bob.

"A few days over, in fact," I said.

"Sorry to hear about the leg, does it give you much trouble?"

"Not really," I said, "and Julie reckons I'm going to do a bit of tap dancing later on."

By ten past eight everyone had arrived and Bob stood on a chair and blew a whistle. When the noise had settled down Bob said, " Ladies and gentlemen, we have a very important guest with us tonight. He has just returned after five years service with the Gunners overseas. As you will know, Albert lost a leg at Alamein and he not only wears the Africa Star Ribbon, but the Military Medal as well. Ladies and gentlemen, I hope that you will give Albert a rousing welcome home."

Well, they clapped and cheered and stamped their feet and someone started up '*For he's a jolly good fellow*'. Julie clung to my arm and we were pushed into the middle. I don't think that in all my life I had been so near to tears. I only hope that I wasn't expected to make a speech, because all I could manage was, "Thank you all very much, it's nice to be home."

As we moved towards the chairs, Julie said, "How was that for a welcome home?"

"A bit overdone, if you ask me," I said.

*   *   *   *

The three-piece band struck up a slow fox-trot. "Come on," said Julie, "forget your old leg and come and have a dance."

Julie flung her arms round my neck, brushing my face with her hair, and with mock severity I said, "Julie, you are not supposed to dance like this, with all the lights full on and all."

But Julie pulled me closer to her, her curls were dangling and touching my eyes, and said, "You will just have to change your dancing teacher then. I can't help it if I get a little spoony, I've had to wait five years for you to come home. And, another thing, I am not going to let you out of my sight, all the girls have got their eye on you. You are quite a hero round here."

I looked down at Julie, bright-eyed and precious and with the lights of the brass oil lamps catching the splashes of gold in her hair Julie could have been a film star. My heart was filled with a new enchantment. She possessed a faint, subtle aura of untouched reserve and I knew that she could have any boy in the room. She was wearing the little gold brooch that I had bought for her in the Garden of Gethsemane, Jerusalem. "Julie, I said, "there isn't a girl here who can hold a candle to you, especially with that sexy, low-cut dress and all."

"In that case," said Julie, catching hold of my arm, "perhaps you will be good enough to take me outside for a little cuddle?"

The moon shone serenely over a silent world and as we closed the door a falling star had just drawn a line of pale fire halfway down the Northern sky.

*   *   *   *

The night was dark and a few drops of rain were falling as we rode back to Newton Green and breathed in the damp wind that blew into our faces. After taking Julie home I quietly stole up the creaking stairs of my father's cottage to my bedroom. It was past one o'clock, but my mother hadn't gone to sleep. "Are you all right, Albert?" she called out from her bedroom. "Leg all right?" she asked, "hope you haven't been doing too much."

"It's as right as rain," I said. "Goodnight, Mum."

I was tired but my mind was still churning and in the dead hours of the night I had my old recurring nightmare. It was always Stuka dive bombers and usually I dreamt that I was in the Desert, but tonight I was with Julie in the middle of her father's farm and the Stukas were flying in from the west. The air was black with them, "Run, Julie," I shouted, "Run for the ditch." But Julie didn't appreciate the terrible danger and stood transfixed, as if mesmerised by the bombers. The Stuka leader waggled his wings and put the plane into an almost perpendicular dive, with the banshee sirens and the bombs starting to fall ... screaming down ... This was the stage when I always woke up. I must have called out, as my mother came in with a night light.

"What is it, Albert?" she said.

"Just a dream."

"Shall I make you some tea?"

"No thanks, Mum," I said, "I'm O.K."

Ever since the Siege of Tobruk, when we were contained in the Fortress for two hundred and forty two days, I had had nighmares two or three times a month. During the Siege our gun positions had been attacked four times by Luftwaffe dive bombers. They had all been horrific experiences and one of the raids had left eight of our Troop Gunners dead.

All this was three years ago and I cursed myself for feeding my imagination, for my stupidity and my lack of self-control. I can tell you now, in the final band of my life, that I have continued to have these frenzied nightmares in the coinage of my brain for over thirty years.

CHAPTER SIX
Julie Puts a Proposition

After two weeks of disembarkation leave I reported back to Woolwich. I was sent on a short, Senior Instructors Course at Magdalen College, Oxford, and then posted to the Royal Artillery Training Regiment at Aldershot. My job was to instruct potential artillery specialists, mostly straight from university, in the intricacies and mysteries of specialist artillery work and technical gunnery. This included the salient features of ballistics and ammunition, the various calculations and fire disciplines, the procedures for transmitting fire orders and the rules and modes of counter bombardment. The course began with systems of setting up a troop of guns in parallel on a predetermined zero line and the course ended with procedures on a Divisional 'Stonk' concentration when perhaps as many as sixty guns could be trained on one target. The procedures and the answers to all our problems were carefully inscribed in the various artillery training manuals and the pamphlets which were issued in an ever progressive stream by the War Office, the Master Gunner and other high fliers in the field of artillery training.

I had two distinct advantages over my classes of students. Firstly, I had done it all for real and, secondly, I had access to all the artillery training manuals in their many volumes, and like many a school teacher in their first year on new work, it was relatively easy to keep one lesson ahead.

In the year of 1945 this grinding war was slowly but surely being won by the Allies. German armies were being pushed back into her boundaries and with the American and British Forces attacking from the west and the Russian Army from the east, the German Nation was being squeezed into submission.

*   *   *   *

One Sunday afternoon, in late April, when I was on weekend leave, Julie said, "I've been engaged to you for nearly six years. The first thing you did when we became engaged in 1939 was to clear off overseas for five years, leaving me on my Jack Jones. Not many girls would have put up with that. We have wasted a lot of time and it's time we got married."

"Can't do that, Julie, darling," I said, "We've nowhere to live."

Julie stood carelessly with her hands in her trouser pockets and her pale blue scarf loose in the wind. "We have, if you play your cards right," said Julie, full of secret information.

"What do you mean? Much as I love you, I'm not living in a tent."

Julie put her arm through mine and said, "Mum and Dad seem to have taken a shine to you, and they've been talking."

"Sounds interesting," I said.

Julie always took a bit of time coming to the point. "Dad was planning to hand over the farm to Kevin after the War." Kevin was Julie's brother who had been gun layer on my gun in the Desert and, sadly, been killed during the Eighth Army advance into Tripolitania, after the Alamein Battle. Julie went on, "So now that Kevin's gone, Dad says that he would like to give the farm to you and me. Half for you and half for me."

"Julie. *Julie*. I can't believe it", I said, "and where would your Mum and Dad live?"

"Well, Dad grew twenty two acres of Kersey White Clover, two years ago, and he kept it for seed. You'll never believe this, but the seed came to over a thousand pounds. That was enough for Dad to buy that pretty, little oak-beamed cottage next to the Post Office.

"All this sounds too good to be true, to be given a farm and a farmhouse and all."

"Well," said Julie, "Dad says that you have had five years fighting for your Country and if it hadn't been for people like you he wouldn't have had a farm to give you at all. And when poor Kevin was killed, he wanted you to take his place."

"I can't imagine a more generous offer than that," I said.

"It's only a hundred acres."

"Oh, that's a big farm, "I told her.

"That's all settled then," she said, flinging her arms round my neck.

$$* \qquad * \qquad * \qquad *$$

During those early Spring evenings of 1945 we were able, from our Depot at Aldershot, to witness the long formations of British heavy bombers flying out on their nightly raids over Germany. One April evening we counted over eight hundred, four-engined, Halifax and Lancaster bombers, heading south east for military and industrial targets in Germany. This was followed the next day by four hundred American B175's in a series of tight formations, setting out on their deadly daylight bombing missions.

The massive, relentless bombardment of Germany from the air, directed by Air Marshal Harris, was at its height.

$$* \qquad * \qquad * \qquad *$$

On 30th April 1945 news came through that the hated German Dictator, Adolf Hitler, knowing that his days were numbered, died by his own hand in a distant Berlin bunker. His was the maniacal spirit that had tried to create a master race and had hypnotised and brutalised millions of ordinary Germans.

On the 4th May, Field-Marshal Montgomery received the surrender of all the German Forces in north west Germany, Holland and Denmark. The War in Europe was over and won and on May 8th, V.E. Victory Day, the peace in Europe was signed.

In thousands of towns and villages throughout the Country the black-out curtains were removed from the windows and after more than two thousand nights of dim glimmers of light and shielded darkness, Britain, once again, was ablaze with light.

However, the War was not yet over. The Japanese Army, Navy and Air Force were still fighting in the Far East and the Allies had still to demolish the war machine of the martial forces of the Land of the Rising Sun.

CHAPTER SEVEN

The Wedding

On 9th August I was taking my class in Number 2 lecture room in the Training Regiment at Aldershot. I had dished out some graphs and tables to the twenty six young soldier students when there was a sharp knock at the classroom door and Colonel Harding, the Commandant of the Training School, entered, followed by the Regimental Sergeant Major.

Colonel Harding was a big man with short ginger hair, parted in the middle, and a neat ginger moustache. He was very much a self-made man and in civilian life had been a fruit and vegetable salesman in the Borough Market and Spitalfields. He had been educated at a State School in Islington and when he spoke there was a trace of the Cockney accent. He was definitely not out of the top social drawer and despised those with an upper class drawl. There was the occasion when one of his younger, over-educated Officers, referred to fire power at 'fah pah'. Colonel Harding asked him what the devil he was talking about!

I put down my piece of chalk and brought the class to attention. "Good morning, Sergeant Cooper," he said. "Tell your class to stand easy. The R.S.M. stood by the door and Colonel Harding moved over to my desk in front of the blackboard. He pushed his stick under his arm and said, "I have some good news. It has just come over the wireless that the Americans have flown another B52 over Japan and dropped a second atomic bomb on the Japanese ship-building centre of Nagasaki. The Japanese claim that over seventy thousand people have perished. Japan is already suing for peace. Carry on, please, Sergeant Cooper, but don't let up on your training. We must stay prepared, as there may be problems with Russia and Eastern Europe in the years to come."

*   *   *   *

Julie and I had decided to get married on the 1st September at Newton Green Parish Church. When the 'Village' knew that the wedding was 'on' they piled in with offers of help.

The ladies of Newton Green Women's Institute collected from their friends and relations tightly rationed butter, tea and sugar.

Charlie Adams, who dealt in horses and ponies, called round one Sunday afternoon in his pony and trap. Charlie said that he would like to take Julie and her father up to the Church for the wedding in his horse-drawn waggonette and bring Julie and I back for the reception. Charlie had won many prizes at the Suffolk Show with his high-stepping Hackneys.

Dick Robinson, who lived at Newton Halland, was President of the Newton Green Young Farmers' Club. He telephoned to say that at their last meeting the wish was expressed that ten of the Young Farmers, in smocks and wellingtons, should form an arch with hay forks outside the Church door for Julie and me.

Old Jake Dash, now heading on for eighty, said he would be pleased to cut the grass with his scythe and bagging hook and to see that the churchyard was tidy.

The Reverend Quartius Trussel, who had not only christened me and my brothers but also almost everyone in the Village, put the date in his diary.

Three weeks before the wedding I received a letter from Colonel Rupert Coleman, my old Battery Commander, who had been awarded the D.S.O. and the M.C., in the Desert. Colonel Coleman was now stationed on a coastal gun site on the East Coast. He had heard that I was getting married and I received the following letter.

"Dear Albert,

I hope that you will not mind me calling you 'Albert' but we served for so long together in the West Suffolk Yeomanry that I hope you will not be offended. Colonel Harding, who I met up with at Boodles last week, tells me that you are getting married at Newton Green on September 1st, and I hope you will not regard it as complete impertinence on my part to ask if Peggy and I can come along to your wedding. We should deem it a great honour if we could do so, I shall always remember signing the citation for your Military Medal in the Desert.

Please do say if it is either inconvenient or embarrassing for you or your family, but Peggy and I would feel very, very privileged to meet your new wife and to have the opportunity of sharing your happy day.

Yours sincerely,
Rupert Coleman.

We wouldn't have dreamt of inviting Colonel Coleman to our wedding as we didn't think that he would wish to come. Colonel Coleman was the eldest son of Sir Alwyn Coleman, a distinguished diplomat, who had been Ambassador in Rome and High Commissioner in New Delhi and Madrid. Colonel Coleman's sister had married Sir Bernard Yates, who, it was said, owned half of Leicestershire. Mrs. Coleman was an Honourable and had sprung from one of the pre-eminent families of the landed gentry in Buckinghamshire.

Julie and I were as pleased as punch that Colonel and Mrs. Coleman wanted to come to our wedding, but it put Mum and Dad into a bit of a flutter. "There's only an Elsan in the Village Hall," said my mother.

"Don't you worry about that, Mum," I said, "the high-bred families are like Royalty and they train themselves to go for long periods without resort to an Elsan or anything else. You can't just break off when you are planting a tree or launching a ship to go and have a wee."

*   *   *   *

I had been to see Colonel Harding, the Commandant of my Training Regiment at Aldershot, for permission to have a few days off to get married. The Colonel said that would be no problem, but that he would expect me to get married in 'Blues'.

"I think," added Colonel Harding, "that there are a few dress uniforms in the 'Q' stores and some of them haven't been worn. I'll write you out a chitty."

The Royal Artillery Blues uniform consisted of a dark blue baretha dress jacket with gilt metal shoulder badges and silver buttons. The trousers were of the same colour as the jacket with a single scarlet stripe. The cap was also blue, with a scarlet band and a blue welt round the crown. The long black boots had spur boxes and spurs attached to the heels.

It was a handsome rig-out and you could fancy yourself in 'Blues'.

*   *   *   *

The day of the wedding arrived. Sandy Evans was my Best Man and he drove us to the Church in his pre-war Morris Eight. He parked the car on the verge beside the Church notice board and we gingerly climbed out, intent that our well-pressed uniforms stayed neat and that there was not a speck of dust on our 'Blues'. Sandy passed me his handkerchief to polish my already gleaming toecaps. Sandy, having been a Regimental Sergeant Major, was now a Lieutenant and Assistant to the Town Major at Dover. He was immaculately turned out, with highly polished Sam Browne, shining shoulder badges and silver buttons gleaming in the afternoon sun. I was proud to have him as my Best Man.

As we passed through the tiled roofed churchyard lychgate and down the gravel path I looked up towards this old Norman Church, weathered and softened by age and time. The magnificent oaken iron-bound door and three beautiful stained glass windows, long painted with pigments fused into their surfaces, stood shaped and solid against the background of rustling elms. This aged mellow stone and flint edifice, with its square built-tower, had witnessed the Christian worship of countless, parsons, choirs and vergers over the generations. Its heavy creaking door had opened wide for farmers and farmworkers, with their ruddy faces and for the patient tradesman who worshipped in its cloisters. The time-worn stone floor had felt the light step of the children and the nervous tread of bridegrooms over the long, long years. It had witnessed the women in their bonnets and bustles and young soldiers on leave from the Wars.

To the right of the gate stood two large marble family tombs, each enclosed in black spiked railings. The tombs were a memorial and a monument to benefactors and worthy citizens of an earlier century, now lying in their pretentious vaults – a commemoration of their grand doings.

Sandy and I were met at the Church door by the Vicar who shook hands with us both and led us in.

The humble Parish Church was packed. It seemed as if the whole village was there. Ten members of the High Barton Singers, in their red gowns and white ruff collars were in place in the choir stalls. Henry Seaton, who was Assistant Organist at Norwich Cathedral, had been persuaded to come to Newton Green for the wedding. All eyes turned as Sandy and I walked over the quarried stone step and took our places in the pew under the lectern.

We were both used to parade grounds and inspections. A high state of spit and polish were second nature to us and we had both worked hard to be a credit to the Royal Horse Artillery. Having seen the War through from beginning to end and survived it all, we were perhaps a little arrogant. The Army had probably made us that way. I recalled the occasion when the Regimental Sergeant Major at the Royal Artillery Base in Cairo was telling the Sergeants on the Parade Ground to, "Hold your heads up, walk tall and look as if you own the bloody place."

Julie arrived ten minutes late. I wasn't too surprised as Julie was often late, but as her favourite Aunt Dorothy said more than once, "She's worth waiting for." Sandy and I stood up and took our places in front of the Vicar. The organ struck up and I felt compelled to glance round at Julie on her father's arm as she walked, like a princess, slowly up the aisle.

She was so gorgeous that my heart missed a beat. In her grandmother's wedding dress she was serene and composed and her long golden hair was catching the shafts of sunlight that streamed through the south window. She was the loveliest bride in the world and my heart was full. "Eyes front," whispered Sandy.

"Don't be insolent and mind you don't lose the ring," I said. The Vicar heard us and gave a little smile.

*   *   *   *

And so I took this woman, no longer a 'Spinster of this Parish', to be 'My lawful wedded wife'. Walking slowly down the aisle, after signing the register in the vestry, and Julie with the composure of a goddess on my arm, we turned through the Church door and into the brightness of the afternoon.

The ten Young Farmers from the Middlesham Club, in white smocks and shining wellingtons raised their hay forks into an arch and we passed through into the cameras. It took us nearly twenty minutes to reach the Church gate, where Charlie Adams was patiently waiting for us with his high stepping Hackney, Lavenham Princess, and his four-wheeled waggonette. Charlie, spruced and smart in his brown 'show' suit and wearing his bowler hat, sat in the driving seat. The reins were lying loosely in his left hand and the whip held firmly in his right. Charlie's twelve year old son, Tom, in his best suit and bow tie, stood at the horse's head. Sandy helped Julie into the waggonette and I climbed in beside her.

.V. Kneale·

The leather had warmed in the sun and there was that balmy smell of paint and polish and leather. Charlie had completely repainted the waggonette in light green and yellow.

"Matches my bouquet and the bridesmaids' dresses," said Julie.

"Bit of luck, that was," I said.

"It wasn't luck at all," said Julie, squeezing my arm, "Charlie and I had a little discussion about that in Charlie's harness room, six weeks ago."

"If you're as bright as that," I said, " I reckon you may be worth the seven and six I have just paid for the Marriage Licence."

Plucking at my arm, Julie smiled and said, "Mum thinks you've got a bargain."

"Seven and six is a lot of money," I said.

The soft chestnut coat on Lavenham Princess, Charlie's champion mare, now champing in the shafts, shone like polished mahogany and a little sweat was beginning to show on her smooth flanks. Charlie raised his bowler hat and turned round to us, "Ready?" he asked.

"Ready," I said.

"Righto, Tom, climb aboard beside me," called Charlie. Tom stepped into the waggonette and Charlie, with a clicking of his tongue and a crack of his whip, gave Princess the orders she had been waiting for. Princess, high stepping, head high, blinkers aloft and ears pricked, was on her very best behaviour. We had over half a mile to go to the Village Hall and there must have been thirty people lining the road and waving to us between The Dog and Duck and the School. As we drew near to the School gate I could see that four of the children were holding up a banner which had been planned and coloured under the watchful eye of Miss Bonner. The banner read 'Good luck to Albert and Julie'. I could also see that Danny Norton and Mary Cope, both aged ten, were holding up their cameras.

"Could you pull up, please, Charlie."

Charlie gave a tug on the reins and with a low, "Whoa there, gal. Whoa, gal," the sleek mare was brought to a standstill. Young Tom leapt out of the waggonette and stood by the mare's head. "Don't stand too near the wheels," said Charlie, anxiously, as the children pressed closer. "Don't want to git you run over."

The two little Watkin sisters, aged eight and ten, were holding a silver horseshoe which they handed up to Julie. Lavenham Princess seemed to know that she was being photographed and stood stock still, head high, steeled and steady as a rock. As we waved the children 'goodbye', a few tears began to roll down Julie's cheek.

"You can cut that out, "I said, "crying like that on your wedding day."

"I can't help it, Albert. I'm so happy and I didn't think that the Village would turn out for us like this."

"The people round here think a lot of you and your Mum and Dad," I said giving her my handkerchief.

It was well known in the Village that Julie was a great help to Emily and Aggy Cook, two old spinster sisters, who were now in their eighties. They lived in an old cottage at the bottom of Cuckoo Lane. Julie had gone into their house every Saturday morning to tidy up and to do their shopping and she saw that they had their 'meals on wheels'.

"They also think a lot of you, Albert," she said, brushing the three stripes on my sleeve lightly with her fingers. "You know, Albert, all these people waving to us are welcoming you home from the War."

*   *   *   *

Like most village halls in 1945, the Newton Green Hall was primitive but it had rendered good service over the years. There was no electricity and no drains. The washing-up water had to be carried in buckets from Mrs. Doris Weaver's kitchen, next door.

The District Council, in spite of having one or two very hygiene conscious ladies on the Health Committee, closed their eyes to the shortcomings of the sanitary arrangements. As Jim Bucket, our part-time rat and mole catcher, always said, "Can't see why they want toilets in the 'all when there's a twenty acre medder at the back."

Most of the Village wedding receptions consisted of a substantial sit-down meal. There were none of these silly little thin sandwiches and stupid little cakes. The repast was referred to as a 'Meat Tea'. Permanently etched on my memory was the occasion when Mr. Jessop, who enjoyed his provender, was invited to a relative's wedding and where canapes and puny trifles were the main source of nourishment. He had partaken of a delicate pastry vol-au-vent, a very small salmon sandwich, which he said was 'the size of a postage stamp', and a piece of 'mousetrap' cheese which was impacted on the sharp end of a cocktail stick. When he was then offered a cheese straw he had remarked to Mrs. Jessop that, "If the food was as good as the samples, he wouldn't grumble."

Julie and I walked into the Hall. The tables were loaded with food. Not much sign of rationing here and it was clear that many of the people in the Village had gone without something so that we could use their food coupons.

Mr. Jessop had given us three of his Game Cross Light Sussex capons and my father had supplied two legs of pork. On these occasions a barrel of beer was considered obligatory and Alf Tappe, the landlord at 'The Dog and Duck' had had a word with the brewers about 'a returned wounded soldier' and all that. The result was that we were given a barrel of Best Bitter, with the compliments of Adnams, which they had delivered direct from their old established brewery in Southwold.

Two people who seemed to be enjoying themselves as much as anyone at our wedding reception were Colonel and Mrs. Coleman. As Happy Tattersall said later, "There weren't no side about them and they weren't a bit proud."

It has to be said that Colonel and Mrs. Coleman were married in very different fashion and style to our modest village wedding. The Colemans, in fact, had had a real Society wedding before the war, and had been married in the Guards Chapel in London. Their wedding reception was held in the House of Lords and the Princess Elizabeth was there and several members of the Royal Household. It would undoubtedly have been in a setting of refined and unembarrassed good taste. The Colemans, however, were having a real old chat with Mum and Dad and Mr. and Mrs. Jessop. They were cheerful and laughing and even Mum looked happy. Colonel and Mrs. Coleman had given Julie and I a beautiful antique silver clock for a wedding present. It must have cost a hundred pounds. Julie's father had asked Colonel Coleman if he would be good enough to propose the health of Julie and me.

*   *   *   *

When Colonel Coleman stood up to make his speech, I recalled the many times that I had seen him standing up and talking to us in the Desert. He would probably have been standing on a small hill of sand or on the tailboard of a 15cwt truck and addressing his O.P. Officer, his G.P.Os. and his Battery N.C.Os. He would be giving us a situation report and orders. We would be grouped around him, our hands clasped behind our backs, shirtless, long haired and bearded, with dark skins and faces, blackened from the years of sun.

I recalled in particular the occasion at Mersa Brega, in 1941, when we were under a savage, hostile tank attack and Rupert Coleman, in his old battered cap, standing on the tailboard of his 8cwt unarmoured truck, was defying the enemy to kill him. Enemy shells were exploding all around us and our two troops of guns were only a hundred yards apart and we were firing at ranges of two thousand yards and he was calmly scanning through his field glasses the escarpment in front of us. He was looking for enemy tanks coming over the crest. Major Rupert Coleman, as he was then, was coolly giving orders to his two Troop Commanders over the wireless and generally pressing the 'No Panic' button. He had earned his D.S.O. that day.

Colonel Coleman began, "My wife and I deem it a very great pleasure and honour to be with you on Albert and Julie's wedding day. Albert and I served together for nearly five years in the Middle East and most of that time was spent in the Western Desert. Albert was the best Gun Sergeant in my battery and I was only two hundred yards away from him when he was wounded at Alamein. As you will know Albert was in a reserved occupation and didn't have to go to war. I had been aware for some time, in Egypt and Libya, that Albert was keen to get back to Suffolk and now I know the reason why! Julie is a beautiful girl and she makes a stunning bride. They really deserve each other and we all wish them the very best of luck, good farming and a very happy life together."

*   *   *   *

Julie and I caught the early afternoon train down to Padstow and that evening at dinner we sat at a table by a tall window overlooking the Camel Estuary. Julie was looking terrific in high heels and sheer silk stockings. She was wearing a daringly cut white chiffon blouse and a long black skirt and this contrasted with the cool look of her skin. The waiter brought us a special fish soup and we each had a lobster followed by some local raspberries and Cornish cream. We finished a bottle of the house white wine between us and Julie became rather flushed and chatty.

"Julie, you're tipsy," I said.

"No, I'm not," she said, with a merry giggle. "It's just that my little heart is leaping with joy." Her eyes were sparkling and I saw her flow of happiness and I knew that I loved this girl more than anything else in the world.

Later, with soft white hands and gentle fingers, she led me to the bedroom, there were glimpses of black and apricot lingerie and her love was like a fire in her blood.

*   *   *   *

In the morning, after a pot of coffee in the lounge overlooking the sea, we walked the beautiful and spectacular Cornish coastline down to the Bedruddin Steps. The gulls were crying overhead and on the shore there was the gentle lapping of the sea water at our feet as the foam swirled in the rock pools.

The following day we crossed the Camel Estuary. I took Julie's hand and we walked through the fields of daisies over to the half-buried church in the middle of the old golf course at St. Enodoc. The oyster-catchers were busy digging their long yellow beaks into the turf and in the murmuring background, the soft pulse of the sea wafted and turned. Standing there by the sunken ruins of the old church, a condensed essay of history, and holding Julie's hand, I felt a warm cushion of serenity and peacefulness, far removed from the years of the harrow of war, and there was still that knot of thankfulness that I had been one of the survivors and I had been one of the lucky ones.

*   *   *   *

That night, in the still hours, I had one of my recurring nightmares and my heart was pounding like a trip hammer. I dreamed that the Stuka dive bombers were diving down on Julie and me. I must have called out and when I woke Julie said, "You were shouting 'Take cover'. What is it? Is it those old aeroplanes again?"

"Yes," I said.

Julie put her arms around me and said, "Get back to sleep, Albert."

I said, "Sorry, Julie, but I can't sleep."

Julie snuggled up to me and drew me close towards her and I felt her warmth. "I know how to get you off to sleep," she said.

CHAPTER EIGHT
Back to the Land

"God did not will that the way of cultivation should be easy"
Cicero

I was demobbed at Aldershot, in late September 1945, with six medals, a badly fitting 'demob' suit and a kit bag full of memories. A quarter of my short life had been spent in the Forces and, at long last, my Army days were over and I was a civilian again.

*   *   *   *

For the first two months after my demobilisation I spent every day on the farm with Mr. Porter. I had a lot to learn and, although Mr. Porter was a bit old-fashioned, he was a good farmer, and he was pleased to show me round and the way he had been running the farm.

The farm was split into seven fields of between five and twenty acres. The ordnance survey gave the following information:-

Barn Field	14.16 acres
Hopcroft	15.66 acres
Hurrels	8.00 acres
Broadshots	19.82 acres
Hodges Piece	16.17 acres
Beggars Bread	21.44 acres
Chandler Wood	5.35 acres

There was also a three acre patch at the back of the house known as 'Ants Garden'. Altogether the farm was just over a hundred acres. It was a nice compact unit and the land sloped well to the south.

A few Light Sussex hens and about a dozen highly hued bantams scratched up the dust in the loose soil around the farmhouse gate.

The red, tin roofed cattle barn, with its built-in pigeon loft at the far end, stood about forty yards from the farmhouse. Inside the barn and knee deep in straw and smelling of soft warm dung, mangels and sugarbeet pulp, were fourteen white-faced Hereford cross Friesian bullocks. They were a picture of gently moving colour on which to rest the eyes. When Mr. Porter took me round, these solid placid creatures were sniffing and licking their coats with their rough tongues or slobbering over their troughs of beet pulp and rolled barley. Others were pulling in mouthfuls off a yelm of barley straw. I could hardly believe that these magnificent soft dewy-eyed beasts had been given to Julie and me.

Mr. Porter walked in among them and stroked their soft flanks. "This one," said Mr. Porter running his hand over a bullock's firm rump, "is out of Tom Corbett's, Hereford cow that won a 'third' at the Bath and West."

I very much doubt if the bullocks ever made any profit. Mr. Porter always seemed to pay too much for the store cattle when, on a market day, in early Spring, he bought them from the Irish cattle dealers. The Irishmen shipped bunches of their store cattle over to Middlesham Market, from Rosslare. The cattle were usually somewhat thin and bony as they had come through an Irish winter.

Will Horsnell, a bullock man from Upper Melcham, always said that although he grumbled about his bullocks not making any money, you had the pleasure of their company and you made some good dung.

Another farmer of the old school, Jack Musgrove, was equally philosophical and assured us that 'the bullocks' may not make any profit but they would 'hold your money together'. I never could make much sense out of that, when there was no inflation and you could get 4% on deposit at the bank.

On the top half of Hurrels eight acre paddock behind the barn, and contained within a, single wire, electric fence were eighteen black and white Wessex Saddleback sows, running with a Large White boar. The Large White cross Wessex was very popular, and the blue and white offspring, sold as weaners, would usually make a good price in Middlesham Market.

These young 'store' pigs were bought by 'hard-headed' men known as 'fatteners' or 'swill feeders'. They possessed vast steam cookers to process, cook and sterilise large quantities of second-class bulky food.

*   *   *   *

Some of the more progressive London Boroughs collected and cooked their own swill and sold it to the farmers at a considerable profit. This cooked swill was known as 'Tottenham Pudding' and a shovelful of cooked swill looked very similar to a shovelful of pig dung. I can tell you that one day when Josh Bishop, who had a small-holding near The Malsters Arms, was feeding swill to his pigs he was called away to help Herby Dodd with his cow that had had garget and red water and had now got hung up in a gate. When Josh returned to his pigs, he looked at the barrowload of swill, with a shovel stuck into it, standing by the pig pens. He took off his cap, scratched his head and said, "What was I doin' along o' these owd pigs – afeedin' on 'em or amuckin' on 'em owt?"

*   *   *   *

Mr. Porter's little pigs were weaned when they were eight weeks old and the sows would usually come on heat three days after weaning. As the gestation period for a sow is three months, three weeks and three days, if all went well the sows would have two litters a year. Some of the best sows would rear more than twenty pigs in a year. Mr. Porter, who kept meticulous records, informed me that old Amy, an ear-torn, thrice ringed matron, who was five years old had reared over a hundred piglets.

Mr. Porter was always very particular when he was selecting his young gilts for breeding. He was adamant that they all had to have at least twelve well-spaced teats or 'dinner plates' as Mrs. Porter called them. As Josh Bishop had always said, "It ain't no good an owd sow hevin' twelve pigs if she hent got only ten tits."

They say that 'Pigs is muck or money' but I knew that they must have been making a lot more profit than the cattle and I made a mental note that, when Julie and I were settled in, the pig herd should be expanded.

CHAPTER NINE
Broadshots

The time-worn 18th century farmhouse, Broadshots, stood, like many farmhouses in East Anglia, in a slight hollow. A gravel chase, a hundred yards long, led up to the house and on the left stood the imposing thatched barn which was orignally used to store corn for the parson's tithe. The partly moated homestead was walled in lathe and plaster. It had four bedrooms, uneven walls and yards of stone floors and cold, dark passages. There was a multi-shelved dairy and a flyproof larder in the cold north end of the house and the small upstairs bathroom, facing north east was as cold as charity. Mr. and Mrs. Porter had not been brought up to be molly-coddled. The spacious kitchen, with its high ceiling and its Aga cooker spreading its warmth day and night, was the heart of the house. The cream-coloured four oven Aga with its viteous enamel tops, a coal-fed Ideal boiler for heating the water and a magnificent Welsh Dresser were Mrs. Porter's main pride and joy. The cosy ample warmth of the kitchen had saved the lives of many piglets and new-born lambs, and it had warmed and dried wet waterproofs and leggings, rubber boots and black sou'westers.

The solid oak kitchen table, as heavy as a sack of wheat had, over the years borne the whole weight of Mr. and Mrs. Porter's weekly shopping on market day. There would be great joints of meat, cans of fly spray, blocks of rock salt for the horses, sheep dip, rat traps and paraffin for the lamps. There was suet and flour and, in season, sugar and Seville oranges for the 200lbs of marmalade that Mrs. Porter made every year. All these effects and chattels were unloaded from the back of Mr. Porter's van after a day at the Friday market. Other stores would be unloaded direct into the storeroom with its heavy green door where the stockpile

41

would include repaired horse collars, broom heads, plough shares, Stockholm tar and pig wormers.

Mr. Porter negotiated for everything he bought, whether it was for a tractor or a pair of socks, and when the shopkeepers saw him coming they often added a little bit to the price to allow for the discount that Mr. Porter would require.

Occasionally Mr. Porter would take in to market a dozen cutters or porkers, and, as he bought his weekly joints of meat from John Briggs, who had two butchers' shops in Middlesham, John was expected to buy Mr. Porter's pigs or at least run them up in the bidding.

*   *   *   *

The Sunday afternoon after we moved into Broadshots, Julie and I were standing in the big unheated hall. A healthy aspidistra stood on the low brass table under the small lattice window with its coloured lozenge-shaped panes set in lead. On the strong shelf behind the aspidistra reposed a bust of Victoria. 'The Monarch of the Glen', in its enormous gilt frame, hung on the wall to the right of the mahogany hat rack and on the left hand side was a cheap print of 'Highland Cattle'.

A grinning fox's mask, which had been known to frighten visiting children, and the head and antlers of a many-pointed stag were fixed to the wall over the parlour door and a black-painted, iron, umbrella stand, inside the hall door, held a black rolled umbrella, two horned walking sticks, with silver collars, an old hockey stick and Mr. Porter's twelve-bore Churchill gun. The floor was covered in patterned linoleum with a strip of dull brown carpet down the middle. On the wall, halfway up the stairs, in detached isolation, hung two soft pictures of lowering sunsets on the Isle of Arran.

Hanging on a nail beside the grandfather clock was a Zulu spear which, unbelievably, had been brought back by Julie's great uncle from the South African War.

We moved into the roomy parlour. There were geraniums in the windows. At the chimney end the eyes would be drawn to the great open, brick fireplace with the 3ft long basket in the grate with its shovel, poker and tongs. It would take very sizeable lengths of logs and timber. The small curved bricks at the fire back housed the ornamental plate of iron dated 1673, all built by 17th century craftsmen.

In the recess under the large south facing bay window, settled in impressive dignity and transcending in importance all the other household equipage, reposed Mr. Porter's dark-stained, roll-topped desk. Here Mr. Porter had kept his old-fashioned double entry filing system of book-keeping. Here were records of crop rotations going back forty years. In the files were plans and maps of the farm drainage systems, the yields of corn and potatoes over the years, and invoices, statements and delivery notes.

Mr. Porter would permit no produce to leave the farm without a ticket, the registration number of the lorry and the signature of the driver.

Julie and I went out through the back door into the orchard with its neglected apple trees now high in grass and nettles. There were overgrown raspberry bushes and an elderly plum tree. A path of cinders wound its way from the back door to a number of chicken coops standing in the nettles. We also found sacks of logs and a bag of rancied chicken meal stored in the outside privy.

At the south-west corner of the orchard stood an ancient oak tree, twisted by years of struggle with the wind. The light evening breeze was ruffling the water in the pond. Night was falling and the homing rooks were coming in to roost and a great splash of crimson spread across the sky. All was peaceful and Julie and I stood in a dream, holding hands. We breathed in the fresh, sweet air, the smell of the soil and the tang of the cattle yard.

We loved it all and couldn't believe our good fortune.

*   *   *   *

For Julie and I these were glowing and exciting times. We were both determined to make a success of the farm and we had been brought up to consider hard work a virtue. Until every beast had been fed and racked up for the night and all the jobs that should be done that day were done, you did not, as Mr. Porter used to say, "shut the stable door". In those early days Julie and I worked from dawn to dusk. We were learning all the time and were absorbed in the magic of growing plants and the turning of the soil. There was also the fascination of the progress and transition of the various livestock ranges and the miracle of the reproductive cycle.

*   *   *   *

That first year ended with a severe winter. The farm was a drab tapestry of snow and ice and the winds cut like a knife. Water pipes were frozen solid and almost the whole of Christmas Day was spent, with freezing hands, carrying water to the livestock.

Every day, until the end of the first week of the New Year, we took a horse, with frost nails in his shoes, and a four-wheeled wagon carrying a 150 gallon tank, down to the river. Here we broke the ice with iron crowbars and to fill the tank we carried filled buckets of water up the snow-covered river bank.

*   *   *   *

There came the days of early spring, when the earth shivered with the forcing of the resurgent secret life which had slept under the winter earth. There were mornings of shimmering mists and rich moments of discovery. It was like an ancient rhythmic song, a rise again of nature's benediction.

In the months of March and April the wind was chasing the rain and the air was cool and sweet and the long toss of nature was boxed in creative inspiration.

*   *   *   *

They were days of feeding and watering and littering and mucking out. In the turn of the year there was planting and weeding and swinging the starting handle of the fractious Fordson. We were involved with cotter pins and shackles and drill settings and wheel changes.

They were wonderful, those early days, and for Julie and I these were days of excitement, development and expansion of the farm business.

Most mornings Julie and I were up at 6am and Julie fed the hens at Broadshots. It was traditional for the farmer's wife to have the egg money. She also walked round the sheep before breakfast. Julie always insisted that whenever possible I should have eggs and bacon for breakfast. However, there were many occasions when we were busy with drilling or cultivating when I didn't come in for breakfast at all, and I would have a sandwich and a flask of tea on the tractor, and I've seen the time when I hadn't stopped the tractor to eat at midday either. The priority was to get the work done, and then, hopefully, we could relax afterwards. Mr. Porter had always rightly said that during seed-time and harvest, one fine day is worth five bad days. The early farmer never had to borrow from the latter and that the difference between a good farmer and a bad farmer was a fortnight.

Certainly, at seed-time and harvest it was unwise to lose a moment on our heavy land which, after an inch of rain, would sometimes turn into a quagmire. Under these wet conditions it was better to keep the tractors off the fields altogether, as the wheels of the tractor compressed the land and destroyed the soils structure. I had often wished that we could afford a crawler tractor with wide tracks, as they created less pressure on the land.

In the Spring and Autumn, when hopefully the dust was blowing and when we were busy with seeding and cultivating, it was possible to work with the tractors for long hours. I would take over the Fordson tractor from Happy at 6.30pm. We would fill up with kerosine and top up the oil and water and with lights on the tractor I would work through until 2.00am.

During the cold November ploughing nights I wore a heavy Army overcoat, buttoned up to the neck, and thick gloves and mittens. Overhead, the dark canopy of the East Anglian night was girded with myriads of pulsating stars.

As time slid by in the duration of those dark night hours with the fresh smell of the earth turning under the plough, foxes and deer would cross within thirty yards of the tractor and stare with turned heads – their bright eyes shining in the shooting beams of the headlights. Occasionally, plovers disturbed in their night rest in the stubble or a hunting barn owl would fly lazily across the light path. The nocturnal wild life appeared with growing faith and trust, confident, inquisitive, curious and happy living with man.

During that first year Julie and I made a profit of three thousand pounds.

CHAPTER TEN
The Escape

Our neighbour on the north west boundary was Archie Jolly. Archie was getting on a bit and he lived and farmed at Brickend Bury, a very good arable and livestock farm of three hundred and thirty acres. Archie, ruddy-faced and cheerful, always wore his dirty, old trilby hat on the back of his head, and he didn't worry too much about anything.

Archie was reckoned to be a 'cattleman' but he never could keep his cattle in. It was said that he had never erected a decent cattle-proof fence in his life. Most of Archie's fencing consisted of the three hundred year old straggly hedges which ran round his meadows and if cattle got out through a hedge, Archie would stick an old bedstead in the gap or push in two or three hawthorn bushes. It was said that the hedges wouldn't keep a blind old cow in, let alone a bunch of hungry bullocks and a couple of bulling heifers.

It was towards the middle of May, several months after we had moved in to Broadshots, that Archie's cattle were running through my sugarbeet. I wasn't too pleased, I can tell you. The beet were half-grown and the field of twelve acres looked a picture – not a weed in it – and here were Archie's cattle galloping all over it. Not only were they stomping about but they were also eating the green leaves and if they got too many fresh beet leaves wound into them, the poisonous oxalic acid in the leaves would soon make hungry cattle turn their toes in.

Julie had phoned Archie and he had driven round by the road in his old, battered Morris Oxford, sagging on its clapped out shock absorbers. As Archie climbed out of his car, a big roan bullock, with its tail in the air, decided to head off towards the road. Archie began to run after it, accompanied by his so-called cattle dog called Moffit. Moffit was really worse than useless, and he had no real

46

idea of driving cattle but he did enjoy chasing them and if he could get within range he would delight in giving the cattle a quick nip on the heel. At that particular moment the cattle were wildly galloping with the big roan in the lead followed by the two bulling heifers and Moffit lying about fourth.

The bullock beat Archie to the roadside hedge and Archie, who carried too much belly timber, started to blow. I shouted across to Archie, "Are you all right, Mr. Jolly?"

And Archie said, "This job's getting a bit too much for me, Albert. I don't know as I want to be tearing about after cattle at my age. I git out of breff and git winded too easy." Archie, still breathing hard, was leaning on his stick and he said to me a very surprising thing. "How would you like to run my farm for me, Albert?"

*   *   *   *

The bullocks by now were getting more and more excited and were running half wild. With Moffit snapping at their heels, they were galloping hell for leather straight for my Barn Field where I was growing a new wheat variety for seed. Julie, who had left feeding the orphan lambs to come and help us with the cattle, saw that Archie was puffing and blowing and she said, "You go back to your car, Mr. Jolly. We'll get your cattle in for you."   Julie was wearing a white shirt and newly laundered, green overalls. She was Archie's favourite woman and you could see that he was glad to see her.

The bullocks, revelling in their freedom, were now dashing towards the gateway which led into the wheat field. Julie, realising what was happening, rushed to head them off. She made it just in time and, with her stout hazel stick, she stood in the gateway and faced the charging bullocks. You can never be absolutely certain with cattle that have temporarily gone a bit wild, but Julie stood her ground and the galloping cattle half-checked and then slewed round to the left.

An hour later the cattle were back in their home paddock with heaving flanks and covered in steamy sweat.

*   *   *   *

Julie and I were walking back to the pick-up. "Clever wasn't I, to cut those bullocks off?" said Julie, impishly.

"Trying to show us up."

"Not much trouble to show you old men up," she said.

"You winning the eighty yards, under sevens at primary school has gone to your head," I said.

When we reached the pick-up I climbed into the driving seat and Julie popped in beside me. "Julie," I said, "do you know what Archie just said to me?"

"What?" said Julie, showing very little interest.

"He said that he was getting too old for farming and chasing cattle and how would I like to run his farm for him."

"Do you think he meant it?" she asked.

"Well, I never got a real chance to ask him, with all those bullocks running about."

"Right," said Julie, "After lunch you can go straight over and see Archie and find out if he meant what he said or if in a weak moment he was talking out of the back of his hat."

*   *   *   *

In the afternoon of our invasion by Archie's cattle I climbed into the truck, and drove over to see Archie. I found him in the cattle meadow by the river, with his billhook and slasher, cutting a few blackthorn bushes to stick in the gaps where the cattle had pushed though.

"Hullo, Albert," he said, "Thanks for your help with the bullocks this morning and I hope they didn't do too much damage to your beet. Can't keep the buggers in."

Archie picked up another prickly bush with his two-tined fork and laid it in the gap. "You know what they say about a hedge, don't you?"

"No, " I said.

"They say a hedge is there to keep horn from corn."

"I don't reckon you have told your cattle that, " I said, with a smile.

"No," said Archie, "but let's hope they've done enough runnin' about for a bit."

"I reckon that roan bullock of yours is a rig," I said "and the two heifers are bulling so no wonder the bullock gets edgy and also," I went on, "the warble is on the wing and stinging up their legs." I didn't say that the main reason the cattle got out was that there was hardly any grass in the meadow and the cattle were hungry. Archie was mean with the nitrogen fertilizer that he spread on the grass in the Spring.

Archie said, "You know I said something about you running my farm this morning."

"Yes," I said, "you did say something about it."

"Well," said Archie, "what do you think?"

"I don't know quite what you mean by running your farm for you," I said, "I should have thought that if you want to retire that it would be better if you let me rent the farm from you or you could even sell it to me."

"I shouldn't want to sell it," said Archie. "I shouldn't have anywhere to live and I should miss the cattle and one thing and another."

"If you sold it, I shouldn't want your house," I said. "I should only want to buy the land and buildings and there's no reason why you couldn't continue to live in your house for the rest of your days. If I bought it, perhaps you could keep an eye on my cattle instead of paying rent."

"To tell you the truth," said Archie, "if I did sell the farm I'd as soon you and Julie had it as anybody."

"If you are prepared to consider selling," I said, "I should be very interested."

"Well," said Archie, "I should want a good price for it. I've farmed this place for over fifty years and it's getting a bit too much for me. None the more for that, I don't intend to give the farm away."

"I wouldn't expect you to give the farm away." I said. "We should have to have the farm valued but if you considered selling then I'd have to think about it and I'll come back and see you in a day or two."

CHAPTER ELEVEN
Albert Visits the Bank Manager

The next morning, after a sleepless night, I made an early appointment to see Jim Cook, the Manager of the Middlesham Branch of Barclays Bank.

I knew full well that I should have to keep my wits about me, and I have to admit that I had a nip of whisky before I left home, which I hoped would fortify my resolution.

I was met in the large banking hall by Mr. Bevan, the Chief Clerk, who ushered me along the corridor and into the Manager's sanctum. 'The Presence Chamber', as Julie called it, had its walls and high ceiling covered in rich panelling. Opposite the door stood an impressive leather-topped desk and the floor was overlaid with a deep green carpet.

When I entered, Mr. Cook, in pin-striped suit and glasses, got up and shook me by the hand. "Good morning, Mr. Cooper," he said. "Take a seat."

As I sat down in the leather-backed chair, Mr. Cook picked up the silver cigarette box on his desk and said, "Cigarette?"

I was more or less off cigarettes but I said, "Thank you, Mr. Cook," and picked out an expensive-looking, cork-tipped, flat-shaped Turkish affair and Mr. Cook fired his lighter.

"And now," said Mr. Cook, sinking into his chair, "what can I do for you?"

"Well," I said, "I might want to buy a farm and if the deal comes off I should want to borrow a lot of money."

"Would it be Archie Jolly's farm, by any chance?" asked Mr. Cook.

"Sounds as if you've had your spies out," I said.

"Well it's my business to keep an eye on what's going on, and I know that Mr. Jolly is finding that the farm is getting a bit too much for him," said Mr. Cook, "and I also know that he is your neighbour."

"You've got all that right first time," I said, drawing on my cigarette.

"So what have you in mind, Mr. Cooper?"

"First of all," I said, "I want to find out what the farm is worth and then, if Mr. Jolly and I can agree a price, I should want you to lend me the money."

"Have you done a budget and cash flow?"

"Well," I said, "I've only had time to do some rough figures but I reckon that, providing costs don't suddenly escalate and prices for corn and livestock remain more or less as they are, then, with a bit of luck, I should be able to clear my overdraft after the third harvest."

I passed over my two sheets of figures to Mr. Cook and he said, "I see that you have budgeted for wheat yields of forty hundredweights an acre. Is that not a little optimistic?"

"No, I don't think so," I said. "The yields of wheat seem to be increasing every year and there is talk that some of the varieties that are in the pipeline have very stiff short straw and will stand up to high doses of nitrogen. The plant breeders are claiming that in a few years time there will be yields of over four tons an acre."

"Just before the war," said Mr. Cook, "an average of twenty two hundredweights an acre was considered to be very satisfactory."

"Yes," I said, "and there should be a market for all we can produce. We are importing millions of tons of wheat from America and Canada."

Mr. Cook rang for his secretary to come through and photo-copy my budget and cash flow figures. "Yes," said Mr. Cook, "and we must hope that never again does the government neglect agriculture. As far as a price for Mr. Jolly's farm is concerned, not many farms have been sold in this area during the last few years and I think that the last one would have been Thorley Hall which was purchased by one of the Pension Funds for £56 an acre. I should have thought that that is about the price you would have to pay for Bridgend Bury. After all, the farm lies well, and nearly half of it has been tile and mole drained in the last five years. In addition, it has three useful farm cottages. What would you do about the farmhouse?"

"Archie has more or less volunteered to keep an eye on the cattle," I said, "so if I bought it I should hope to let him live there for the rest of his days, rent free."

"That's a very generous offer," said Mr. Cook, leaning back in his chair. "So, if you can agree a price with Mr. Jolly and wish to borrow the money then you and your wife will be required to deposit the deeds of Broadshots with the Bank. I have to tell you though that in loaning you this money the Bank would be going out on a limb, as the collateral of the value of Broadshots Farm wouldn't cover the price and value of Mr. Jolly's holding. However, having seen you and having heard of your plans for the farm and, knowing that your father-in-law has banked here at Barclays for over forty years, I will recommend the loan to Head Office, and you can take it from me that it is almost certain to go through."

Mr. Cook rang through for coffee and offered me another cigarette. I was beginning to feel on cloud nine and couldn't wait to get back and tell Julie.

*   *   *   *

Five weeks after my appointment with the bank manager Julie and I drove into Middlesham for an appointment with Henry Bell of Bell, Thain and Hinder.

Bell, Thain and Hinder had their old-fashioned offices in Market Street and they were the largest and oldest established firm of solicitors in Middlesham. They had as their clients many of the larger and most successful farmers and landowners in the district.

It so happened that Henry Bell was also solicitor for Archie and, together with my accountant, Greg Sanford, an agreement was drawn up which was satisfactory for us all.

The price of Archie's farm was to be £56 an acre. It was calculated that with the maturing of his life policy with the N.F.U. Mutual and the bit of capital that he had in the bank, and the unknown quantity of cash which Archie was reputed to have under his bed from selling point-of-lay pullets during the war, he would be able to live in comfort for the rest of his days. Archie would also have the proceeds of the sale of his implements and farm machinery and he would live in the farmhouse rent free.

"Best day's work I ever done," said Archie, as we shook hands after signing the deeds and the various documents.

I dare say that we really had done Archie a good turn whereas Julie and I would be saddled with a potentially crippling overdraft which we might never be able to pay off.

*   *   *   *

So, together with Broadshots, Julie and I became the proud owners of four hundred and thirty two acres of some of the best land in West Suffolk.

When Archie had gone, Mr. Cook said, "You will require the Bank to lend you money for three hundred and thirty acres at £56 an acre, which is around £18,000 plus £3,000 to run the farm for twelve months, so if I give you an overdraft limit of £25,000 you should be able to manage comfortably until next harvest."

"What interest should I have to pay?" I said.

"I can let you have the money at one and a half percent over Bank rate," he said. "At the moment the Bank rate is four percent."

Julie was doing some mental arithmetic. "That," she said, "is £1,300 a year."

"It represents paying the equivalent of £3–£4 an acre rent, and we ought to be able to manage that all right," I said.

None of us at that time suspected that in ten years time our farms would have been worth £2,000 an acre.

As we drove home Julie said, "Now with all your land holdings, don't carry on as if you are the Duke of Westminster, and don't go and get big headed and imagine you are running the Royal estates at Sandringham."

"I shall have to join the Country Landowners' Association," I said, "and you will have to get a hat for the Game Fair and what is more," I went on, "don't imagine that you are going to stop working on the farm. I don't want any of this getting involved with the Women's Institute or the Church or the Flower Club women."

"I'll have you know that there are no 'women' in the Flower Club," said Julie, "only ladies."

"And what about the Women's Institute?" I said. "Surely there must be some 'women' in the Women's Institute?"

"You are a clever Dick," said Julie, "and it's a funny thing that you mentioned the Church, because Mrs. Jennings has asked me to be secretary of the Parochial Church Council. I said that I was too busy feeding livestock on Sunday mornings and was often unable to get to Church by ten o'clock. Mrs. Jennings is People's Warden and I think she reckons you're a slave driver."

"Can't think why she thinks that," I said, "I've taken you to the pictures twice in the last month and obtain seats in the front row of the balcony."

"And a fat lot of good that was," said Julie. "You were so tired both times that I had to wake you up for the British Movietone News. We don't look like having too many holidays with this whacking great overdraft."

"Well," I said, "we can't leave the cattle, pigs and sheep for long. We'll go for a long holiday when the ship come up to the front door."

I think," said Julie, "that you would be better off, now we have a few more acres, employing a foreman rather than trying to do everything yourself. It doesn't do your old leg any good for you to be tearing around all the time."

"You could be right," I said. "Maybe one day we shall be able to afford to farm without livestock and then we could get away for a week in the Winter and in the Summer we could probably have a bit of free time between haytime and harvest."

I drove the pick-up through the gateway and parked at the end of the brooder house. Julie and I climbed out. "You would be a miserable old devil if you hadn't got your animals to worry about," said Julie, "and as a matter of fact," she said, catching my arm, "I don't really want a holiday at all. I'd rather stay here with you and our old farm. You never know, one day we might own a thousand acres."

Julie stood there in her jeans and loose-fitting denim shirt, bright-eyed and pretty as a picture. "I love you, Julie," I said, "and if you want to be secretary of the Parochial Church Council, just go ahead."

"I'll settle for doing the Church flowers once every six weeks," she said, "and I'd never forgive myself if one of the old sows farrowed and laid on one of the little pigs while we were at Church or away on holiday."

CHAPTER TWELVE
Ted and Happy

When we were negotiating with Archie he said that he hoped we would take on his two men, Ted Kettle and Happy Tattersall. Ted and Happy had been with Archie for over twenty years. In fact, they had both worked at The Bury since they had left school at the age of fourteen. Their first job on the farm had been when they were on their school holidays and had been picking stones in the field for fourpence a bushel. Ted and Happy knew every inch of the farm. Ted was Archie's horseman and he had drawn hundreds of furrows with his old wooden plough. Happy drove the tractor and looked after the bullocks when they were brought in off the grass. Ted and Happy lived, with their wives and children, in a pair of cob and thatched cottages in Crippins Lane up a grassy track on the bottom road. For their cottages the two men paid Archie a rent of two shillings a week.

The pair of cottages were three hundred years old. They were time-warped and cocooned in restful isolation. They were built to a past quality and were a soft tribute to builders, joiners and thatchers of long ago. The outer walls were black-tarred weatherboard and the ancient oak timbers were as sound as a bell. The staircases consisted of a heavy ladder with less than a forty degree slope. There was no additional insulation on the old mediaeval roof and they had been built without fuss and the disruption of the modern council building regulations.

Archie had recently had built two very small rooms by the back doors of the cottages and had installed pull and clank toilet systems.

The Ministry of Agriculture had laid down in the War that a farm required two or three men for one hundred acres, but we thought that we could run four hundred acres with Ted and Happy and Julie and myself, with Mr. Porter as longstop.

*   *   *   *

It was just after a quarter past four on an early June evening. The farm and village lay under a great sheet of blue liquid sky and there was the low buzz of foraging bumble bees. Ted was in the stable after having spent the day, since half past seven, with his two horses mowing the rye grass and fescue mixture in Beggars Bread. It had been a very satisfactory day, and the only trouble was when the reciprocating knife on the mower had run into an old bike wheel that some urban motorist had thrown over the hedge. The mower knife was smashed but fortunately Ted had taken out with him a spare knife, with newly sharpened sections, ready for such an eventuality. He was now back in the stable beside Marshall, his furrow horse. The stall, with its manger and tethering ring, had stout oak partitions and a well-laid, indestructable, blue brick floor. Ted was wisping Marshall down with a hean of straw. Marshall had just been fed and was alternately munching his bait of crushed oats and a handful of molasses, and blowing through his nostrils. Every now and again Marshall would pull at his hay, racked above the manger. The stable had that rich, delicate smell of corn and horses' breath and soft, dunged straw. No accomplished artist with a practised hand could translate in full paint this peaceful scene. There was no way he would be able to capture the aroma and the ambience and the satisfaction of Marshall's full dinner. Neither could he have painted the soft smiles of fortune that ran in the horseman's mind. The artist would also be unable to portray the gentle rustling of the sparrows under the roof tiles and would be hard put to interpret onto canvas the thin film of ancient dust which hung on the cobwebs round the walls and windows of the stable. Ted took the stable broom round the walls of the stable and harness room, to shake off the cobwebs, about once a year.

On this rare glory of a late afternoon in early summer the thinning sun lay full into the stable doorway and caught the splashes of gold on Marshall's broad chestnut backside. Ted wouldn't have swapped Marshall for any two horses in England.

Happy Tattersall had been working his tractor all day, with its narrow row-crop wheels, in the baulked up ridges of potatoes in Hopcroft Field. Hitched on the three point linkage behind his tractor was a Danish-made spring-tine cultivator with flexible tines, and attached to the cultivator was a set of light harrows which ran over the top of the potato baulks to scratch out the weeds. Happy had been pleased with his day's work and had now returned to the farmyard to rack up his bullocks. Most of the bullocks were now out to grass, but the two most promising ones had been kept in and were being coddled and specially pampered for the Middlesham Christmas Fatstock Show where glory and renown accrued to the winner of the fat cattle classes at this prestigious annual event.

Happy had fed his bullocks on a few pounds of crushed oats and newly ground linseed cake, and was now on his way back to the mixing barn. He was carrying an empty hessian bag which had contained the special bullocks' ration, and a two-tine fork for shaking up their bed. The sleeves of Happy's flannel shirt were rolled up and his flat cap was on the back of his head. His weskit had lost all its buttons and his red face shone like a pint in the sunlight.

*   *   *   *

Happy was a cheerful character. He had a deep voice and, wearing his corduroy trousers and with a red and white handkerchief round his neck, he would visit the 'Dog and Duck' on a Saturday night. After he had had a pint or two he had been known to lean on the bar and give a rendition of his own version of 'The Farmer's Boy'. Give him a game of darts and another pint or two and wait for the drink to kindle his veins and he'd honk away at 'MacDonald's Farm' half the night. Give him a shilling and he would stand on his head in the pub yard for five minutes. He had been known to come home late at night and when the clock on the mantelpiece told the wrong time he'd been known to hit it with a stick.

Happy's wife, Mildred, was short-waisted and set at odds. When Happy came home from the pub late at night, toad-bellied and bleary-eyed, and she could hear him singing all the way down the road, there was considerable jaw jaw and division in the camp. It was the signal for Mildred to stick the bolster down the middle of the bed.

One night Happy came out of the pub singing at the top of his voice "Roll me over in the clover" and Walt said, "Oi dun't know why Happy's singin' that. When he gits home he wunt be no good ta she. In this tarradiddle he ent wuth a spoonful of frogs' spit."

*   *   *   *

Happy parked his fork by digging it into the heap of steaming dung that lay outsde Ted's stable and hung his empty bag on it. He walked over and stuck his head inside the stable door to have a word with Ted.

"Howy gittin' along then, Ted?"

"Not sa dusty, Happy."

"Finished Hopcroft then, Happy?"

"Yeah, got that lot done, Ted. Lot of fat-hen on the baulks and Oi put up a couple a' owd hares."

"They loike ta lay up in the taters. You'll have to git a whippit, Happy."

Happy was licking his cigarette paper. "Dun't want one a' they long legged owd buggers. Oi'd rather hev a gallon a' beer."

It so happened that Happy made his own beer – what he called "Poor Man's Brew". He made it by boiling a small quantity of malt and hops together in a kettle and he had been known to mix with his beer some home made turnip wine and, we suspected, a proportion of meths. At any rate, he had once offered a mug of his mixture to Rex Trotter. Rex, who was our local vet, said that he thought the concoction was lethal, and would probably dissolve gall stones and he was certain that it would eat through the cylinder block of a Fordson tractor in twenty minutes.

The East Anglian Show was a week away.

"Goon' ta Show, Ted?"

"Shan't goo fust day, moight goo a' Thusdy."

"There ent sa much drink ta what there used ta be on the merchants' stands. Oi reckon if ya goona git a drink you'll hev ta start afore the buds is up."

Ted stopped wisping down Marshall and threw away his hean of straw.

"Git over there then, Marshall, git over there."

Marshall would have moved obediently if Ted had given him a little push, but Ted liked talking to Marshall and Marshall liked being talked to. Marshall took a quiet pull at his hay and turned his fine head round and looked at Ted – not a sly glance out of the corner of one eye, but he brought his whole head round and gazed for a brief moment at his master with his soft brown eyes. They were both content, the one with the other.

"They say Alf Rattle's takin' his cow ta show, what come second in the 'in calf' cow class larsh year."

"Oi reckon Alf were a shade lucky warn't he? Owd cow were three parts lame – never put the Stockholm Tar on soon enough. When I saw Alf in the mornin' and his cow was lame he looked loike a bloke what had lorst a bob and found a tanner. Oi reckon he'd a bin more happy thrippin' thistles."

Marshall shifted his weight onto his off side. "Stan' still, will yer, you owd sod. You stoopid owd hoss. Stan' still, will yer." Marshall knew that Ted meant no harm and was only making conversation and he munched away at his oats and chaff and gives a short, friendly snort through his nostrils.

"Where d'ya reckon's best place ta git a drink at the Show then, Ted?"

"Reckon if ya say ya wuk for Master Henderson most of the corn merchants'll give ya a pint."

"But we don't wuk for Master Henderson," said Happy.

"No, but he's got over a thousand acres and one way and another spends a tidy lot a' money and they wunt know no different."

The corn merchants and machinery dealers welcomed the farm- workers from the bigger farms onto their trade stands and would stand them a drink or two, and after the Show some of the men would arrive home the worse for wear.

Standholders knew that when the men got home they might just lay the thought in their master's mind that he wanted a new elevator or that new-fangled scientifically prepared formula of BOCM's sow ration was well worth ordering the next time the Guv'nor was in the corn exchange.

"We can always git a drink with the Union if the wust comes to the wust," said Ted. On the NUAW (The National Union of Agricultural Workers) stand, which was always one of the biggest stands on the showground, drink was cheap but not free.

Marshall spread his legs and prepared to stale. Ted stepped back a bit and started to whistle.

"Dunno what yew wanna whistle for Ted. Dun't whistle for me owd bullocks. Reckon owd Marshall can stale alroight wi'out yew hevin' ta whistle. Good job he ent a mare do else yewd hev to stand back agin the wall."

"Oi reckon owd Marshall loikes ta hear me whistle when he's a stalin'. Dun't you Marshall, me owd fella?" It was a powerful discharge and the narrow gutter at the back of the standing, which took the horses' piddle out into the horseyard, gushed like a hot mountain stream.

"Reckon he'll feel a lot better arter that," said Happy.

"How's your Mavis gittin' on then?" said Ted. Mavis was Happy's sixteen year old daughter. She was blonde, pretty and empty-headed.

"Got a job as seckertary," said Happy. Mavis was employed in a very junior position in the Anglian Pension Building Society in Ipswich. As Happy's wife, Mildred, had spent much of her life riddling potatoes, picking peas and hand weeding carrots it was something of a shock to Happy and his wife when Mavis announced that she had got a job in Ipswich. "Well," said Happy, "she gits 'erself up loike a bloody tart when she goo ta wuk an' all she do all day is sit on 'er arse an' talk posh."

"Can't make the young 'uns owt," said Ted. "She could make a lot more doin' field wuk an' she woont hev no bus fare."

"You can't tell these young 'uns nuthin'. These be tarble times."

Happy moved off to his bullocks and sloshed a few buckets of water into the long galvanised drinking trough. "Oid best be gittin' hom," he said. He knew that as it was a Monday when he got home he would have to help his aproned wife, Mildred, unpeg and carry in the washing which hung on the clothes line. Mildred had also mentioned that when Happy had got a minute, he could wash down the paintwork in the kitchen.

CHAPTER THIRTEEN

The Sale

It was ten o'clock on a wet Michaelmas morning and the trees were dripping water, when Bertie Peacock, the auctioneer's elderly clerk and general factotum, stood on a low wooden stool and rang his handbell for the start of Archie's sale.

The sale was attended by about sixty farmers and dealers and there were also present a few sharp shufflers and humbler orders of the peasantry. The assorted numbered Lots represented the lifetime accumulation and clutter of fifty years of farming. The various Lots, much of it in a vintage condition to embellish a farm museum, lay strung out in rows across the horse meadow behind the barn. There were two-wheeled tipper carts and four-wheeler harvest waggons and seed drills and root planters. There were elevators and clod crushers and torn tarpaulins. There were drag harrows, pig crates and iron-wheeled hurdles. These old implements had, over the long years, breathed in the farm's passive vitality as they forged and made headway in the colour and existence of the earth. They had paid their debt to nature.

*　　　*　　　*　　　*

Tom Hughes, of Hughes and Standen, country auctioneers, in brown trilby hat, wellingtons and raincoat, turned up his collar and replaced Bertie on the wooden stool. "Ladies and gentlemen," he said, "it's time we made a start." Tom then gave his usual spiel. "No warranty is given or implied by the description in the catalogue and each Lot is sold in its condition at the time of sale with all its faults, defects, imperfections and errors of description (if any). Purchase money will be paid before delivery and no cheques will be accepted in payment except from persons well-known to the auctioneers. All of Mr. Jolly's equipment is being sold without reserve. It is a wet morning, so please let me have your bids quickly. What am I bid for Lot 1?"

Lot 1 was a heap of old iron and it made seven shillings. Lot 2 was a dung fork plus crome and ladder and was sold to old Pete Filby for five shillings. Lot 3 was a bagging hook, a seed dibber and cob and crowbar.

Next came a log beetle and wedges, two pitch forks, a pick-axe and helvin spade and a gappy-toothed wooden rake. Lot 7 was an ancient wooden wheelbarrow that had seen its best days. Lew Peacock bought it for two shillings, for his allotment.

Lots 9 to 12 were bridles, halters, collars, saddles, bits and martingales. Alfred Copsey, a master saddler in Middlesham, bought the lot.

Lot 13 was a gander and four geese which made eighteen shillings. Lot 17 was a leather crupper.

"What's a crupper?" asked Julie.

"It's a roll of leather fitting under the horse's tail, helping to keep the harness in position," I said.

Lot 15 was a collection of three whippletrees and the back of an old waggon. There was no bid for this Lot and Tom Hughes said, "We'll put it in with Lot 16."

Lot 16 was a swing plough which had the land handle in a straight line with the beam and the furrow handle passed beneath the mouldboard and socketed in the slade. This collection made twenty two shillings and sixpence.

Julie stood there in the pouring rain. She was wearing a green waterproof jacket, corduroy trousers, wellington boots and a green sou'wester. She had her hands stuck deep in her trouser pockets and had given up trying to read the soggy catalogue. She was now closely following the implement prices.

"Why don't you go home, Julie?" I said, buttoning up my old Burberry round my throat. "There's no point in you hanging about and getting drenched out here. Take the pick-up and get in the dry."

"No. I'll stay on here for a bit and watch you men sloshing about in the mud, and I want to see what the Case tractor and the combine make."

Lot 31 was a quantity of brass stair rods. Lot 32 was a cheese press and two round cast iron pig troughs.

"I may not want too much machinery," I said, "I think that we'd better run the Bury round the three year ley."

"Sounds very grand," said Julie, "but what does all that mean?"

"Well, it's all the go with the Ministry Advisory Service at the moment and some of the forward looking farmers are going in for it in the Eastern Counties. The idea is that you put down a third of your farm to grass and clover for grazing by livestock. The ley is left down for three years while it is grazed by sheep and cattle and possibly pigs, and after three years the ley is ploughed up and you take off two crops of winter wheat and one crop of potatoes, or peas, or sugarbeet, and, as the livestock will have put a lot of fertility into the soil, it should reduce the bill for artificial fertilizers. It would also help eliminate the worst weed on this farm, which is wild oats, as we'll never give them the opportunity to seed."

*   *   *   *

Back at the sale, a load and a half of loose hay made four pounds and a pair of dungcart wheels and a milk kindle and churn stand made twelve shillings.

We could see that we were about to stretch our overdraft. I was very interested in purchasing some of Archie's bigger implements and machinery. We bought the American made Case tractor which was only a year old and a three furrow Ransom plough for three hundred and forty pounds. We also bought all of Archie's bullocks, all his cattle troughs and a stack of well-made mixture hay. We also acquired the mill and mixer which was bolted down to the floor of the barn. This was a sound investment as we should now be able to grind and mix all our rations for the pigs, cattle and poultry. This would easily save two pounds a ton against 'bought in' feeding stuffs from the merchants.

What we really wanted was the American built, tractor drawn, Minneapolis Moline combine harvester. This machine, with a six foot cutter bar and powered by the tractor power take off, would cut, thresh and sack up to twenty tons of wheat a day. It was a darn sight better than cutting the corn with the old binder and then stooking it, carting it to the stack and then having all the hassle of thrashing it in the old belt-driven barnwork.

This combine harvester of Archie's had been on a ship that was sunk in Liverpool Harbour by German bombers. The machine had spent two weeks at the bottom of the harbour before being salvaged. We knew, however, that Archie had been using the machine for the last two harvests and he had been very pleased with its performance.

*   *   *   *

Tom Hughes, with his gavel and his clipboard and with the rain running off the brim of his hat, climbed up the three steps of the combine and stood on the sacking platform and said, "What shall I say for the Minneapolis Moline combine harvester?"

"If it keeps a'raining loike this, can't see we shall want a combine, more loikly want a submarine," said Willie Sharp, a familiar wag of the district. A titter rang through the crowd, and it was well-known that a little light relief would sometimes liven up the bidding.

"I'll start it orf at two hundred," called out Jasper Slade, a machinery dealer from Ipswich. I raised my catalogue and Julie squeezed my arm.

"Two twenty I am bid by Mr. Cooper. Who will say two hundred and fifty?"

Dick Butterfield, a tall, gaunt agricultural contractor from Stoke-by-Nayland raised his battered umbrella.

"Two fifty I'm bid," and looking at me closely he said, "and now Mr. Cooper." I nodded. "Two hundred and seventy I'm bid. Is there any advance on two seventy?" And then with almost indecent haste Tom Hughes banged his gavel on his clipboard and said, "Sold to Mr. Cooper."

"That combine was cheap," I said to Julie.

"They intended you should have it," said Julie.

"What do you mean?" I asked sharply.

"I heard old Sam Peggle say to Tom Hughes before the sale, 'Young Cooper is just back from the War and he lost a leg at Alamein and he wants that combine'."

"Christ, Julie, I don't want any sympathy or special treatment, anyone would think I was a cripple. Anyway, it isn't fair on Archie."

"Don't worry about Archie," said Julie, "he's got a lot more money than we will ever have. Just concentrate on buying those two hundred hessian corn sacks, some of them are nearly new and will come in handy to sack the corn off the combine, and then we will go in and have a cup of coffee in the barn."

"At this rate," I said, "we won't have enough money to buy a cup of coffee, we have spent nearly twelve hundred pounds already."

"Worry not," said Julie, cheerfully, "all you think about is money."

"That's not what you say when you've got your nightie on," I said.

When we got back into the old, muddy pick-up, after the sale, we were soaked through and cold, and as we drove home we felt that, in spite of owing the bank umpteen thousand pounds, we had begun to climb the farming ladder.

CHAPTER FOURTEEN
The Hendersons and Others

Our two greatest friends in Middlesham were Peter and Sally Henderson. Peter farmed Wickham Hall, the family farm of eight hundred and fifty acres, which lay north of the Bury road about half a mile from Newton Green. Wickham Hall was an elegant Grade II country house with superb views over the Stour Valley.

Peter and Sally were the same age as us and Peter had been a Gunner in the HAC before the War. In December 1939 he took a commission, and went out as a Second Lieutenant to Cairo, to join the 4th RHA who had already been up in the Western Desert and laying up on the Libyan border for three months. Peter had subsequently taken part in all the earlier desert battles with the 7th Armoured Division during the Wavell Push into Libya, in the late winter of 1940 and the early months of 1941. He was captured when an Italian motorised patrol had surrounded his O.P. south of Bengazi, when both his driver and signaller had been killed. Peter had 'borrowed' an Italian military truck, and had escaped out into the Desert where he, luckily, ran into a patrol of the British Long Range Desert Group. He ended up, seven days later, in Tobruk.

He was sent back to Cairo on a special assignment to take over as second in command of a recently recruited Pack Battery which was being trained for mountain warfare.

Peter, who now held the rank of Captain, arrived with his Battery in Crete, together with mules and 3.7 Screw Guns. Three weeks later, in March 1941, thousands of German parachutists and airborne troops dropped out of the skies and he was captured while defending the aerodrome at Haeraklion, spending the rest of the War in prison camps in Italy and Poland.

Peter had met Sally, whose father was a judge, when she was a Second Officer in the WRNS in Cairo. They had corresponded throughout the War and had married in 1947.

Sally was a tall, slim, good-looking girl with loose fair hair. She had been educated at Wycombe and had gone on to Girton where she had taken a degree in economics. Sally was always well-groomed and she and Peter laughed a lot, cared for each other and lived a fine, warm life.

They had two children, Jonathan, who was born in 1948 and Rebecca, who was born in 1950. I was Godfather to Rebecca and Julie was Godmother to Jonathan. They also had two slobbery, yellow labradors.

Peter had taken a short, farming course at The Royal Agricultural College at Cirencester, but both Peter and I had been 'out of things' for a long while and we both had a lot to learn. We attended conferences, field trials and farm demonstrations and within a few months, with the readily available help from neighbouring farmers and The National Agricultural Advisory Service, we were both able to keep technically abreast of the farmers who had farmed at home throughout the War.

There were great developments in mechanisation throughout the farming industry and new labour-saving machines were coming onto the market all the time. We spent many long evenings at the experimental husbandry farms and the Government research stations.

We flew across to the Paris Agricultural Show and studied the French methods used to maximise the wheat crop.

The word 'efficiency' was used over and over again and with guaranteed prices there was every incentive to increase yields and boost production. We were doing the Government's bidding as the wheat and grain poured into the silos in ever increasing quantities. They were heady days and farming was in a spin.

Jim Turner, the President of the National Farmers Union, when negotiating forward prices with the Government at the annual price review, insisted that throughout the Country farmers should be paid fair prices for their efficiently produced commodities. Certain Members of Parliament were saying that the farmers were being feather-bedded, but the rise in production was spectacular. However, there was still food rationing throughout the land and an internationally known professor, speaking at the Oxford Farming Conference, assured us that the World would be starving within ten years.

There were others among the farming community who talked of the abundance of food which was being produced by the farmers of Europe in response to urgent Government calls for more production. It would, they feared, eventually lead to massive food surpluses.

*   *   *   *

Between our Hopcroft field and Watery Lane lay Farley Wood, and in the wood lived an old drover, and his name was Jacko Crump. The old wooden and corrugated iron hut in which he lived had, in days gone by, been used by the beaters in the shooting parties where they drank their beer and stayed to eat their bevers. Jacko lived alone in the hut except for his sand coloured lurcher, a couple of goats and a few scraggy hens. Jacko's father had been a woodsman and he would cut whippletrees and plough handles, and he had once owned a piebald horse and a four wheeled van which he used for light haulage. Jacko was short and stocky and his hands were cobwebbed with blue veins. With a sack tied round his middle and a big old turnip watch across his weskit, he was a picture of rural simplicity.

On Saturdays Jacko would slip on his Norfolk jacket, put his collar up against the wind and walk the four miles into town. He would return late at night full of beer with his dog and his stick.

During Harvest and other busy times Jacko had been known to milk Mr. Porter's two Jersey cows, chop the wood, beat the farmhouse carpets, separate the milk with the skimmer and turn the handle of the wooden paddled butter churn.

Jacko's weekend began on Friday evening at five o'clock and went on until Tuesday morning. Most winter evenings Jacko would sit with a horse blanket round his knees, smoking his pipe, staring into the fire and spitting into the grate. For liquid comfort he drank meths. Meths, Jacko had always said, was a cure for croup, game leg and gotch belly. From time to time he would pick up the pair of worn bellows to rouse the dull smoky fire into action.

It was well-known that Mollie Smith, a loose-ended baggage from the gipsy enclave in Coppice Lane, would sometimes visit Jacko during the night. Mollie, an unkempt, strapping wench was a real road shammer with a wide behind and pushed out in front, and she knew how to live off the land. She knew how to hide the pheasants' feathers and she had the odd rabbit and would cook and roll a hedgehog in the clay. Mollied lived in a small, brightly-painted caravan with her two illegitimate children. The kids already knew how to dig their fingers under a potato bine to take a couple of potatoes off without disturbing the plant. Mollie was a lively floosy and when she was picking up potatoes or out in the pea field rattling her bucket you could hear her falling into wild cackles of laughter.

The Saturday night drinkers at the Dog and Duck knew that for two bob Mollie would lift her skirt above her head and there were rumours of mayhem in the bales of straw in the barn after closing time.

*   *   *   *

Jacko knew that the local Young Farmers' Club was responsible for the two great corn circles in the wheat field just off the main road. He had seen them with their torches when he was setting snares in the wood. There were half a dozen of them with a stake and a few yards of string. However, Jacko never let on when the local paper sent a reporter with a camera to photograph the celestial deposits. In fact, Jacko had played them along and said that he had seen a spaceship the night the corn circles were made and that 'it was a big as a house'.

George Dace, the veteran photographer from the *Middlesham Chronicle* took photos of the corn circles and also of Jacko. When Alf Potts knew that Jacko's picture was to appear in the Middlesham Chronicle he said to Bert, "See Jacko's 'ad is pho-oh took."

"'Ad his pho-oh took?" said Bert, "'eel break the bloody cambra."

George was dodgy lame in his left leg. "What's wrong then?" said Jacko, "fell down a rabbit 'ole?"

"No," said George, "it's my rheumatics."

"Git stung by a bee, then," said Jacko, "that'll put yer owd rheumatics to roights."

Jacko then said to George, "Wanta see moi ferrets?"

"Yes," said George, and when Jacko put in his hand and brought out of the locker two pink-eyed ferrets and had them eating out of his hand he was well in the way of having his picture on the front page and the back page of the paper. Jacko then put the ferrets back, rolled a cigarette and bet George a gallon of beer that he wouldn't put his hand in the ferrets' locker and bring one out. "I think I'll leave that fer another time," said George, nervously.

"Oi reckon it'll be a day or two afore yew'll put the ferrets down yer trousers in the pub," said Jacko, cunningly. Jacko had earned himself a few bob doing just that.

Jacko then offered to take George out poaching on a windy night, for a fiver. But again George declined. "I only wanna torch an' a little owd ratten adder gun," said Jacko, "to knock 'em orf their perches."

"I'd rather come with you lookin' for golf balls," said George. George, who was a twenty five handicap golfer had seen Jacko out on the golf course with his lurcher doing a bit of ball scrounging. Jacko's lurcher knew what a golf ball was all right!

"You wouldn't hev any golf balls, would you?" said George.

"How many do ya want?" asked Jacko.

"A coupla dozen would do," said George.

"Better take fifty," said Jacko, getting two fertilizer bags, half full of golf balls out of the sink cupboard.

The next night, with the money from the golf balls, he bought beer in Middlesham. He became dead drunk, cock-eyed and tolley headed. He found he was unable to walk home and he lay all night by the side of the road with his dog in a bush of cockbrumble.

*   *   *   *

It was a warm Monday morning in late May when the bent and narrow-gutted figure of Nobby Stripe was edging his way along the lower end of the Village Street. Nobby was short and stocky with a low slung bottom. He could have worn a cleaner shirt and his jacket had seen better days. Nobby, as artful as ever, was past work and was now on the pension. Nobby hunched, unshaven and beady-eyed was poking away at the road edge gutters with his spindle-shanked ash stick. He had nearly reached the well-stocked Village corner stores where flitches of bacon were displayed alongside cases of lard, bags of oatmeal and strings of Middlesham sausages. Nobby was considering purchasing a couple of sausages for his lunch when he encountered no less a person than the Reverend Quartius Trussel.

The Vicar was tripping along quite briskly and was looking vigorous and ethical in his linen jacket. The Reverend Trussel had been along to collect his copies of *The Church Times* and *The Clergyman*, and had also set out twenty copies of the Parish Magazine on the small table at the end of the bacon counter. He had been slightly put out by the sight of a copy of *The Methodist Recorder* among the pile of magazines. This publication of the Free Church was referred to by brother Anglicans as 'The Dissenting Rag.'

"Mornin', Parson," said Nobby, assuming an appropriately solemn expresson and touching his cap as a token of his humility. "'Taint sich a good mornin' as it was yisty artnoon."

The Vicar considered that he might have a brief word with Nobby who was spiritually on the extreme periphery of his fold.

"Morning, Stripe," said the Reverend Quartius, warily.

"Noice rain in the noight, Parson."

"Yes, nice rain. It will do good."

"Speakin' personal," said Nobby, blowing his nose with his fingers, "it'll do more good than we shall."

The Vicar gave a tired smile, "I doubt it, Stripe, but you speak for yourself."

"Could pray fer a drop more rain," said Nobby, drawing his hand up his trouser leg, "but there, it ain't no good a'prayin' fer rain when the wind's in the east."

The Vicar gave a sharp cough and drew out his watch and put it back again. "You could always *try* praying, Stripe," said the Vicar, indulgently, "but I don't think that I saw you in Church last Sunday."

Although he had gone through a pious phase Nobby was known to be rather careless about his religious duties. "Didn't yer now," said Nobby, looking like a didicoy who had been caught by the gamekeeper putting a ferret down a rabbit hole, "Oi reckon Oi must hev bin sittin' ahind a pillar."

Nobby, who sadly had not rejoiced in the enchanted ground and the poetry of religious experience, scratched his head and twitched his toes inside his shoes and said, "To tell yer the truth, Parson, Oi can't remember whether Oi was in Chuch or not."

"Nobby, who smelled of toadstools and fish paste was no Bible basher and was making no attempt to take the opportunity of putting himself right with Heaven. Everyone knew, of course, that Nobby, who was an amiably compulsive liar, was a bit of a street Arab. He had a shakey sense of morality. He was a well-known poacher and he had once been found with forty pheasants in the back of his old van at two o'clock in the morning. He had also been known to threaten keepers.

Nobby had once overstepped the mark and stolen a bike from outside a pub in Swaffham. For this indiscretion he had to fork out a twenty pounds fine, and had been put inside for a week, in what the Reverend Trussel called 'The House of Correction'. It has to be said that the Reverend Trussel had sought divine guidance and had almost abandoned praying for Nobby. However, Nobby's two young grandchildren, Will and Beth, regularly attended the fortnightly meetings of the 'Little Kingfishers' in the Church Hall and when they were asked to choose a hymn they always asked for 'Jesus wants me for a Sunbeam'.

There also reposed the latent fear in the Vicar's mind that Nobby's wife, Amy, could conceivably defect to the Chapel, as she was quite high on Jesus. So taking all in all in the forefront of his thinking the Reverend Trussel, overpassing the deeds of the wicked, considered that Nobby should be allowed a period of grace to find a path between the pits of hellfire and unwholesomeness.

There was no doubt that in Nobby the Vicar had one of his wavering churchgoers but the Vicar always used his best endeavours to harry his flock and to stimulate the latent religious feelings in the community. He knew he would never succeed in making Nobby easily familiar with the works of the Almighty and he had confided to Mrs. Trussell, while in bed, that Nobby was a conundrum in the most various circumstances.

On one, never to be forgotten, occasion at evensong the Vicar had given a little homily on the Lord changing the water into wine. Nobby, who wearied himself to committ iniquity, sat at the back of the Church. He had had more than a skinful at the 'Dog and Duck'. He stood up, unsteadily and holding onto the back of the pew in front, and interrupting the Vicar in mid-parable said, in his loud rackety voice, "Parson, Oi do foind that very difficult to believe," and sat down again.

It was said that the Vicar was greatly confounded.

CHAPTER FIFTEEN
Nipper

It was a Sunday, mid-afternoon, in the high days of Summer. The dust flew about in little earth fountains. In the diffusion of light in the lone high feather of a cloud, rose a golden limb of the resurgent sun. Down below the cricket field the traffic was humming evenly on the main road.

A large flock of marauding pigeons, which had been feeding near the scarecrow and close to the automatic banger in our main crop onward peas, were now wheeling in the near cloudless electric sky. There was a streak of poppies in the corn where the sprayer had missed. The half-ripe ears of winter barley stirred in tender waves below the pig run. They moved in an endless unfurling ripple like the sea in the breathing of the wind.

The nettles and wild buddleias were covered with nervous, darting butterflies. Beside the whispering corn two young stoats were chasing each other along the headland. A nest of skylarks' eggs were on the point of hatching in the lower part of Church Field, which was down to perennial rye grass and Kersey white clover. Wild strawberries sparkled in the woods on the edge of the waggon lane.

Over the brim of the cricket ground, near the sunny side of the thatched pavilion, Poddy Bishop was resting his behind on the fallen trunk of a diseased elm, which had succumbed to the Dutch Elm beetle.

Poddy was twenty four and was the nephew of Nobby Stripe. He was straw haired, podgy and bespectacled in cracked, steel rimmed glasses. He had a high-pitched voice, and at this moment in time, his mind was in neutral as he munched a jam sandwich. He always wore his cap on the back of his head and his concertinared trousers were at half mast. Poddy was wearing a short shirt and his belly showed above his trousers. Two plastic bags were tied to his feet and when he wasn't eating he usually had a short length of string in his mouth. Poddy, you could say, wasn't up to much and had something of a communications problem. In fact, the Village schoolmistress had given him up when he was six. Poddy's thoughts were non-consecutive.

Although Poddy had never owned or ridden a motorbike in his life, he would occasionally walk round the village in a pair of heavy dungarees, a motorbike crash helmet and a pair of aviation goggles.

Poddy was accompanied by his three parts Jack Russell terrier, called Nipper. Nipper lived in a barrel outside Poddy's privy and when he was let off the chain he gave the cats a hard time. At rutting time when Spring and the scent of amorous bitches was in the air, Nipper subjected himself to long absences from the barrel and was a much heard of dog. Nipper's trade mark could be seen round the

villages for four miles around. Little, sharp-eared, three eighths Jack Russell puppies and half grown segments of the canine dominion could be seen piddling around and sending signals of disobedience to their luckless owners. This was all indicative of Nipper's wide circle of friends. Nipper was not noble born, in fact, you could say that he was very low bred. He was thoroughly disobedient and unpredictable and he could put on a very good show of being deaf.

At this particular moment in time, Nipper, who had been in hot pursuit of the shadow of a pigeon, was now capering to and fro chasing a yellow butterfly.

Once in a while Nipper would come to heel if he was called and Poddy was ever hopeful. "Come 'ere, Nipper," shouted Poddy, "leave that owd buttyfly alone."

Nipper cocked an ear doubtfully, but it soon became clear that Poddy and Nipper had different priorities. Nipper had now lost interest in the butterfly and was nibbling a dandelion. He was in an easy frame of mind and was very deliberately minding his own business.

"Come here," shouted Poddy, again, waving his stick.

Nipper, showing considerable indifference, lunged at a fly and then cocked his leg against the cricket roller. He then started sniffing around for a place to lie down.

Poddy had a lisp, "Yew thilly owd thod," he said.

Nipper tried to scratch his ear, lost his balance and fell over. He then lay down by the roller, stretched open his jaws in a leisurely yawn and licked his John Thomas – Nipper was plunging deeper into anarchy.

Poddy lifted his cap and scratched his head, and putting a hand to his back, stood up and straightened himself – as far as his 'artheritus' would allow. He gave a hitch to his trousers and took hold of his stick.

Nipper, who had considerable staying power, knew that Poddy's patience was drawing towards its close, but he managed to show interest and smell the discarded wrapper of a Mars bar. He once more circumvented the roller and, in his own good time, squeezed under the bottom rail of the fence and sidled up to Poddy, wagging everything. Poddy raised his stick, and Nipper, wagging his amiable hindquarters, smelt round Poddy's ankles, rolled over on his back, exposing his little, pink, external male organ and wambled his legs in the air   "Yew thilly owd thod," said Poddy, again.

*   *   *   *

Poddy and Nipper were joined by two loitering youths, Walt Buckle and 'Stumpy' Sloggett. Stumpy had his jacket over his arm, a bag of crisps in his pocket and, with some difficulty as he walked, was eating baked beans out of a tin. Stumpy was sort of sluggish and flat-footed and to tell you the truth, it took some time for a message to find its way from his brain to his voice box. He did a bit of part time, casual work, as assistant to Maxwell Bowser, the local thatcher. Stumpy and Maxwell had been known to spend the whole of a weekday afternoon lying in a heap of straw at the base of the stack or cottage which was waiting to be thatched, in an alcoholic stupor.

Stumpy, who you could say was unaware of the limitations of his knowledge, didn't worry too much about anything. In fact, he had once bought a beat-up old banger, for fifteen pounds, from 'Fishy' Shard, the local shyster, and when he got it home, water was pouring out of the bottom of the radiator. When he hit a small pothole, outside his council house, both the silencer and the exhaust fell off. All Stumpy said, when most people would have been driven spare, was "Well, Oi'll be buggered."

Stumpy's sister, Dot, had twice been arrested for shoplifting but Stumpy was proud of his brother, Harry, who once had a car with wing mirrors and for a brief period had rented a garage with up and over doors. Harry was now on the run from Borstal, where he had been sent for having been caught removing several gallons of oil from Mrs. Jessop's central heating tank. He had also been fined for indecent exposure when he landed a job in a shoe shop in Romford.

Walt, who was wearing a hairy jumper with car badges on it, and who had a face like a fish, had been known to have worked for short periods and had once been paid to scare rooks by heaving clods at them and rattling stones in a tin. For all that, however, Walt had little momentum and he mainly survived as a recipient of Government generosity at the Labour Exchange. He had once taken two hours to put back the wheel on Mrs. Burton's baby's pram. Ben Quinney, the undertaker, had been heard to say that Walt couldn't pull a duck off its nest, and he was about as much good as a fart of fertiliser in a five acre field.

"How yew gittin' on then, Pod?" said Walt.

"Mussen't grumble," said Poddy.

"Yew've got a fair bitta belly showin' between yer shirt and yer trousers," observed Walt. This tickled Walt a great deal and he roared with laughter. As Walt laughed he hit Stumpy.

"What did yer hev ter hit me for?" whined Stumpy, complainingly.

"Can't help hittin' someone when Oi laugh," said Walt.

"Where's yer dog then, Pod?" said Walt.

"Over there in the ditch," said Poddy, pointing to a vigorous disturbance of the undergrowth in a long scatter of earth.

Nipper had stirred into brisk activity and had been determined to dig out the rabbit even if it had gone down to Australia. Nipper was like a mole and had back feet like shovels.

"He's a good owd rabbiter," said Poddy, proudly.

"They say he wunt do nuthin' what you tell it to," said Walt, working mischief and using his well-known capacity to stir controversy. "They say," went on Walt, "you couldn't train ivy up a wall."

"Don't mock Oi, Walt," said Poddy, "you'll drive me to religion. Nipper do wot Oi tell 'im."

"Make 'im come over 'ere then and lie down," said Walt, testing the limits. "All he do is fart and piddle. Do more good if he caught a rat or two."

It is true that on that very morning Nipper had piddled on a box of plants, the front wheel of Poddy's bike, the back wheel of Poddy's bike, a bucket of pig food, each of the four posts holding up the turkey pen and he had irrigated Poddy's row of onions.

Poddy took a hold of his stick. "Come 'ere Nipper," he shouted, hopefully.

Nipper paused pulverising the very earth for three seconds, cocked his head and his little pointed ears on one side and then resumed his programme of rabbit annihilation. The rabbit, in the meantime, had decided to cut and run, and had long since left the area by escaping out of one of the botholes on the far side of the ditch. The botholes had been constructed for this very purpose, and the rabbit was now leisurely scampering alongside a hawthorn hedge halfway to Lexden Common.

Poddy went over, got down in the ditch, grabbed Nipper by his collar and dragged him, unwillingly, to his seat. Nipper stood there covered in dirt, panting from his exertions and drooling with his little pink tongue hanging out. He was wet and in great disorder.

"Now," said Walt, "make 'im sit down."

"Thit down," commanded Poddy, authoritatively, "thit down."

Nipper looked at Poddy, blankly and didn't move. He began to sniff up the wind at his pleasure and his little heart was throbbing.

"Thit down," repeated Poddy, louder than ever.

Nipper, who would much rather have been ratting, or better still, have been playing wheelbarrows with Tiddles, the little Sealyham bitch, behind the Post Office, began silently to whimper. He looked harried and sorrowful. Nipper liked to be liked and was fully prepared at this late stage to make himself agreeable. He had not won the gracious forgiveness of his master, and at this rate was unlikely to be deluged with honeyed phrases. He looked up at Poddy with his little bloodshot eyes, in totally servile and fawning subjugation.

Poddy, who was becoming confident that he was winning this battle of wills, took off his cap and held it high above his head and in his loudest and most threatening voice shouted, "Thit down, Nipper. *Thit down*, will yer."

Stumpy and Walt, greatly tickled, were all eyes and ears. "He ain't gonna sit down," said Walt, cheerfully.

"'Taint so loikely," said Stumpy, "best thing you can do, Poddy, is to have him nootered. He's a dead loss. 'Ee dunt know his backside from a hole in the ground."

Nipper had almost decided to soften hearts by rolling over on his back again and then thought better of it and stood in noble, passive resistance. He was thirsty and wished he was lapping water under the sink. He felt rejected and with his tongue lolling out, he was the manifestation of canine wickedness.

Poddy took off his cap, mopped his face with it and, throwing it on the ground, jumped on it twice and then flinging his arms in the air, in total despair, he shouted at Nipper, "Thtand up then and bugger yer."

CHAPTER SIXTEEN
Silver Rain

Julie, being a working farmer's daughter, had learned to do many things on the farm which girls would not have been expected to do before the War. Julie could pluck a turkey, shear a sheep, harness a horse and skin a rabbit. She could also drive the tractor and thought nothing of rolling or harrowing thirty acres in a day.

However, what surprised me most when I came back from the War was to find that Julie had learned to ride a horse and, in fact, had become rather good at it. During the last two years of the War, Julie had been going up to Lawford Hall, a mile and a half from Broadshots, and had been helping Lady Helena Carrington to exercise and school her horses. Lady Helena was in her forties, President of the area Red Cross and County Commissioner of the Guides. She was an accomplished horsewoman and regularly hunted with the West Suffolk Fox Hounds of which she was Joint Master. Before the War she had won the Ladies Races at numerous Point to Points in the South of England, and the large cabinet in the trophy room was full of silver salvers and cups. Lady Helena was also very keen on dressage and Julie thought the world of Lady Helena's special dressage grey mare, Silver Rain. Lady Helena's husband, a Major in the Life Guards, had been badly wounded in the spine at Dunkirk and had been taken prisoner. He was paralysed from the waist downwards. The Major was repatriated through the good offices of the Red Cross in 1944 but was confined to a wheelchair. Lady Helena had lived at Lawford Hall throughout the War, with Bertha, a faithful retainer who had been maid and general help for over twenty years. Lady Helena had taught Julie to ride and Julie had taken to it like a duck to water. She had exercised with the horses two or three times a week.

*   *   *   *

Late one afternoon, Julie said to me, "Like to come up to the Hall and see me on Silver Rain?"

"Might as well," I said, "now you are in high society, you had better have someone handy to help you on again when you get tipped off."

"You needn't worry about that," said Julie.

*   *   *   *

Julie came down the stairs in hard hat, cream shirt and jodhpurs, with a light whip in her hand. You wouldn't have thought that half an hour earlier she had been mucking out the boar pens. Her golden hair was piled in a net on the nape of her neck. Her cheeks had a healthy glow and her bright blue eyes sparkled in the late afternoon sun. She could have been a well-born lady of the manor rather than the working wife of a four hundred acre farmer with a massive overdraft. *Christ*, I was proud of Julie.

We approached Lawford Hall through the long gravel drive, bordered by blue hydrangeas. The seventeenth century baronial hall, with its thirty rooms, reposed in the centre of a walled country estate. There was a fine walled garden, a spread of greenhouses, a potting shed and a nuttery. The substantial brick stables, with their red tiled roof, were topped by a white timbered weather-vane clock tower.

"A nice little weekend cottage, "I said, as we drove in.

"Shush," said Julie, "don't be cloddish. You are not to let me down Albert."

There were signs that the garden was becoming a burden. Half-wild roses were growing over the nettles and the matted tussocks of coarse grass. A briar was entwined round an old laundry post and dripping from the stable roof were tumbling skeins of creeper. We disturbed, on the edge of the drive, a brightly coloured peacock which flew heavily up into a walnut tree. I drove up to the stables and Jim Butt, the Major's groom who knew that Julie was coming, had Silver Rain saddled up in her box. There was a saddle room with a row of spotlessly clean tack hanging neatly on pegs and racks. There was not a wisp of hay or straw out of place.

"Good Lord!" I said, "you've got a groom to saddle up your horse. You'll think you're Lady Muck and you'll be getting ideas above your station."

"Jim and I get on all right," said Julie, smiling.

"I can see that," I said, in mock peevishness, "I expect Jim calls you 'your ladyship'."

"No," said Julie, "he just calls me Julie."

Jim, short and bowlegged, in khaki riding breeches and leather gaiters, held Silver Rain's head while Julie lightly swung onto the mare's back. Fifty eight year old Jim could establish friendly relations with any horse by blowing down his nostrils. Jim led the mare through the apple trees into the open paddock. The mare, with ears pricked, seemed to be primed with tense, alert quietness, yet somehow touched with a dark invisible fire. Julie laid her hand on the mare's shoulder and Silver Rain, gentle, sensitive and easily alarmed, arched her neck. It was like a flood of ancient understanding and was a whole dimension of life at its best.

*   *   *   *

"Right-o, Jim," said Julie, and Jim let go of the bridle. Julie took up the reins and with straight back and gentle pressure, put the mare into a collected trot in a diagonal line towards the far corner of the paddock. Standing on the bit and with controlled impulsion there was an absolute balance as she worked a perfect twenty yard circle to the right. Coming out of the circle, Julie pushed Silver Rain into a full extended trot, maintaining a constant light contact with the horse's mouth. Here was Silver Rain, commanded at the helm, controlled with a silvery lightness, perfected in extension and balance, steady as a moon rise.

Taking the reins in one hand, Julie did a serpentine of four regular loops and then, with the merest signal, Silver Rain, obedient and supple, was brought to a halt. Julie sat there as straight and motionless as a trooper of the Blues and Royals in a sentry box at Whitehall. The mare stood absolutely stock still, with free immobility and total obedience. They held the position for ten seconds. There was a harmony and confidence and a cherished mutual trust. There was an inner elegance of style. It was tinged with magic.

Julie, applying simple aids clearly and effectively, brought the mare, calm, relaxed and with unhurried movement, into renewed life. Silver Rain accepted the bit willingly and Julie put the mare into a working canter next to a line of beech trees on the south side of the paddock. Exquisite co-ordination between human brain and equine muscles was there for all to see. Horse and rider were so well-balanced that the mare would change her feet and shorten or lengthen her stride by the touch of a leg.

They circled a small stand of maple before turning to the left and, without losing pace, Julie threaded her way back through the line of beeches. With ears pricked and neck arched the mare was responding to every hint and to every signal as if driven by a soft caressing wind. She was changing step at every tree as she threaded from left to right and right to left like a returning swing.

Julie sat there, light as a feather, hands like bees' feet, looking straight between the horse's ears, totally absorbed, maintaining impulsion and flexion and the purity of the paces. The horse's ears were pricking back and forth, eager for every whisper and pressure. A harmonious partnership had been formed of balance and rhythm. Christ, Julie had style. "You know," said Jim, as a bright glint of satisfaction moved in his eyes, "that wife of yours is a born horsewoman."

At the end of the line of trees the silver mare, all fire and full of controlled power and ease, changed to lead, and, tracking left, swung out onto the smooth poll of pasture. There was a spatter of froth on the horse's chest and Julie, with hands light and no obvious manipulation, and with deft turns and changes, did a neat figure of eight and with fluent transition and easy stride, Silver Rain, swishing her long tail, pivoted and side-stepped like a mystery dancer. I was captivated. Julie, serious and concerned and full of self-possession, tracked to the left at an extended trot and riding up to us on the long rein she brought the mare to rest. From the halt she reined back four steps, advanced four steps and reined back six steps between the line of trees. It was with the hauteur of the knights of old and was manifest proof of her complete control. And then it was over. The creative crowning touch was accomplished, thoroughly paced, and sweeping and absolute in its fulfilment. It was a creation full of dark vitality and like a world beyond our world.

Julie, with her slim waist and looking elegant and faintly amused, rode the mare up to us, swung her leg over the saddle and got down. Jim took the mare, with her hide still marked with saddle sweat, by the bridle. Jim, who rode out on Silver Rain most days said, "I reckon she give you a good ride, Julie."

"Yes, thank you, Jim," she replied, "she's perfect."

For my part, I looked at Julie and saw her beauty and her happiness and I hadn't got a thing to say.

CHAPTER SEVENTEEN
The Cart

One Saturday morning, in late Spring, Wilby Potts and Mortimer Trussel, both aged nine and a half and in Class 2b at the Village School, sat in Bob Watson's dusty old cartshed at Newton Hall Farm which was at the far end of the Village. They were perched on the shafts of an obsolete, horse-drawn, hay shaker.

Wilby was the only son of Alf Potts, who was pigman to Bob Watson. Alf could hardly read or write but he had a keen eye for saving the odd copper and always took *The News of the World* because compared to *The Sunday Pictorial* he could get more squares of paper for the outdoor 'privy'.

Alf Potts' great annual foray into the corridors of glory and renown fell in the way of the heavyweight Porker Class at the Middlesham Christmas Fatstock Show. Consequently, Alf paid much attention to the litters of pigs that were born during the first two weeks of August. When these litters were weaned at the age of eight weeks, Alf would select six well-grown matchy pigs, spray them with mange dressing and stick them in a warm well-strawed loosebox, where they received very special attention. Out of the six pigs Alf would, later on, select the four best ones for the Show.

Alf fed these pigs three times a day and there was no doubt about it, the pigs were thoroughly spoilt and never went short of anything. Any spare milk from the cowshed was quietly diverted to the ever-hungry porkers. They had been known to have apples and carrots, and Alf would take his bagging hook out at the back of the Watson's garden and cut them an armful of Comfrey and a few sprigs of Feverfew. Alf swore that the Comfrey and Feverfew kept his pigs healthy. None the more for that, Alf invested (at Bob Watson's expense!) in patent worm and condition powders, as advertised in *The Farmers Weekly*. If the instructions on the label of the condition powders said "feed one packet per pig daily" then Alf would see that they had two.

Alf had tasted glory, and over the last three years, in the pig classes at the Christmas Show, had been awarded one second, one third and one highly commended. It was Alf's great ambition to win, not only the class for heavy porkers but also the enormous silver cup which was presented by the auctioneers for the best pen of pigs in the Show.

It was when it came to the paperwork and keeping the pig records that put Alf and, often Bob, into a state. The trouble was that, as Alf could hardly read or write, keeping records was a recipe for abundant confusion. Alf frequently made inaccurate entries in the well-thumbed Boar Service Register which hung on a nail by the medicine cupboard in the fattening house. Beside the Boar Service Register hung the grain company calendar, showing young ladies in various stages of undress and this also had a disturbing effect on Alf's concentration.

It was a source of great comfort to him to see his pigs grow and bloom and when, at feeding time, the porkers ran towards him and he was able to scratch them behind their ears, every fibre in his body tingled with pleasure.

The gestation period for a sow is three months, three weeks and three days and, times without number, a sow which had been running with the boar in the meadow showed well bagged up and full of milk when, according to Alf's register, she'd got another five weeks to go. The sows all had numbered metal ear tags and if the old sows had been fighting or had mud and meal all over their ears the numbers were difficult to read and Alf would say, "Oi do reckon Oi git they owd numbers middled up."

Alf's son, Wilby, who wanted to be a gentleman farmer, however, was bright for his age and was often given to serious thinking. On this Saturday morning Wilby was thinking as he sat on the shafts of the hay shaker with his friend Mortimer.

The two boys had been over to look at Wilby's three geese. Their names were Pip, Squeak and Wilfred. Wilby had reared the geese from goslings, and it is well-known that it is difficult to tell a goose from a gander and there was some constenation when Wilfred laid an egg. In fact, during the past week Wilfred had laid three eggs and Wilby had taken them up to Mrs. Bright at the Village Shop and had traded in one goose egg for two Mars bars. And so Wilfred's sex-change was not without its advantages, and indeed was in the first water of good fortune. Wilby reckoned he had struck oil.

*   *   *   *

Mortimer was out of a different stable to his friend Wilby Potts, as Mortimer's father was none other than the Reverend Quartius Trussel, Vicar and sole incumbent of the Parish of Newton Green.

The Reverend Trussel was a spare man with thin grey hair and prominent ears. He was an exacting theologian and sometimes at Matins and in moments of resolution and vigour, would preach fire and brimstone at his hapless congregation. He saw it all in virtuous moral clarity and his commitment was made manifest to Jehovah. He believed verily in frugality and austerity and thought much of his own dignity. The Reverend Trussel displayed a critical eye for human frailty and had little time for the young. He was convinced that his son, Mortimer, belonged to a pampered generation and should not be spoiled by an excess of parental affection. He looked forward to the time when Mortimer could be despatched to a well-known boarding school in Hampshire, specially run for the sons of the clergy.

However, the Reverend Trussel was an assiduous visitor of the sick, had a wide concern for humanity at large, and would pray for those in the farthest parts of Christendom. On occasion he would express displeasure at the tight-fisted parsimony of The Diocesan Board of Finance.

The Reverend Trussel could often be seen on his battered old bike, pedalling through the village, dressed in yellow oilskins. He had insufficient stipend to keep up a superior position in the Village and sometimes had to be humble to the County families, to the marked displeasure and tribulation of his wife.

All in all though, the Trussels were a pattern of charity and piety and Mrs. Trussel gamely contributed to the welfare aspects of the Church and the Village and made lists of the sick and needy.

*   *   *   *

So Wilby and Mortimer, the sturdy sons of Alf Potts and the Reverend Trussel, were bosom friends and allies, particularly in moments of adult confrontation.

Wilby spoke broadest Suffolk like his father, and Mortimer, to the everlasting vexation of his parents at the Vicarage, spoke broad Suffolk, like Wilby. Mrs. Trussel had never fully approved of Wilby being her son's friend since she had caught Wilby piddling on her croquet lawn.

After inspecting Wilby's geese the two boys had had a fairly satisfactory morning catching sparrows. In fact, they had caught nearly twenty in Wilby's patent sparrow trap. The trap consisted of an upturned bushel, propped up on one side by a Y-shaped stick to which was attached some thirty feet of string. After placing some pieces of stale bread and cooked, flaked maize under the bushel the boys retired to just inside the mixing barn where they were able to take the string through a crack in the door. When there were deemed to be a well-stocked mob of sparrows under the bushel, Wilby gave a sharp tug on the string. However, after a bit, the adult sparrows learned that the motives of the apparent benefactors that had placed their breakfast under the bushel were not unreservedly in their best interest and became very wary of approaching the trap.

So this was becoming very boring and Wilby picked up two thatching pegs and began beating an upturned cast-iron pig trough. (Wilby had informed his parents that when he grew up he would be a drummer in Henry Hall's band, that is if West Ham and Tottenham wouldn't take him and recognise his undoubted talents as a potential aggressive match winning striker).

Mortimer picked up a flattish stone and threw it at the pond, hoping it would be a skimmer and get more than three Barnes Wallis's off the water.

Wilby decided to trot out his thoughts, threw away his drum sticks into the nettles and said, "Oi know what we'll do."

"What?" said Mortimer. "Cowpat bunging?" Mort wasn't keen on throwing dehydrated bovine deposits at cars on the main road. "No," said Wilby, "we'll make a cart."

"Hain't got na wheels," said Mortimer, dismissing the project .

"Two pairs a' pram wheels behind Dad's woodshed," said Wilby.

"Goo an' git 'em then," said Mortimer, wiping his nose on the sleeve of his jersey, "An' git an ammer an' some niles."

"You git a box, then," said Wilby, "an' we shall want a couple a' bits a' wood fer the shafts. Hullo, here comes Tracy."

Tracy, aged six, was Wilby's sister, whose main ambition was to work behind a counter at 'Woolies'. Tracy had once received much acclaim during a nature class at school. It so happened that two birds had decided to nest in their earth closet. Tracy had said to her teacher, during the nature class, "Pleath, Mith, there is a Wobin's netht in our pwivy."

Tracy was dressed in a clean, pink shift with white socks and black patent shoes.

"What do you want?" said Wilby crossly.

"Nuthin'," lisped Tracy. "Don't want nuthin'."

"Why don't you goo hom' then," said Wilby, thoughtlessly

The corners of Tracy's mouth turned down and she began to cry.

"Blub. Blub," said Wilby, "goo on, turn on the tap."

Tracy cried louder than ever.

"Well, you can stay if you loike," said Wilby magnanimously, "Only don't git in the way, do else you'll hev ta shuv orf." Tracy, whose world was balloons and gingerbread men, brightened, "Oi'll git you an apple, if you loike," she said.

"Git two, then," said Wilby, "you moight as well git one fer Mort."

Tracy turned on her heel, tucked her frock in her knickers and scampered off on her important mission, happy as a young magpie.

*   *   *   *

Wilby set off to search for the four, rusty, pram wheels which lay hidden in the nettles behind his father's woodshed. While he was there he also 'borrowed' his father's claw-hammer and grabbed a handful of three-inch nails from his father's toolbox. Wilby was expressly forbidden to use his father's tools and he knew that if his father caught him at it he would be threatened with a clout round the ear.

By the time Wilby arrived back in the cartshed Mortimer had procured a stout tea chest from the Reverend Trussel's small garden shed. The tea chest had been used, by the Vicar, to store miscellaneous items of potential usefulness. When Mortimer removed the heavy lid, the contents proved to be a small bag of dahlia corms, a spare chain for the old 14" Suffolk Punch mower (the lawn mower which had been replaced seven years ago), some powdered chalk for marking the neglected tennis court (now out of use), a magnificent heavy adjustable spanner, a can of greenfly spray, a couple of mole traps, a small quantity of rancid chicken meal, four brass stair rods and the head of a log beetle. Mortimer tipped this lot out on the floor and carried the tea chest to their temporary workshop in Bob Watson's cartshed.

"Roight," said Wilby, "let's git started."

It could be contemplated, with some certainty, that when the Reverend Trussel opened the garden shed door and saw that the tea chest had gone, and that its contents were spilled all over the floor in a heap of great disorder, that he would be hard put to think thoughts that were saintly.

Tracy, who had returned with two apples and was dying to help, said, "I know where there's a couple of pig pats, they'd do orlroight for the shafts."

Wilby had to give it to Tracy, she was bright all right, and a couple of pig pats would make a decent pair of shafts.

A pig pat consisted of a piece of white painted board, about a half inch thick and about three feet long and three inches wide, with a handle shaped at one end. They were used to guide pigs around the show-ring and were issued free to pig farmers by the big feeding stuffs companies to promote their pig feed and the various ration supplements. The feeding stuffs companies were particularly keen to distribute these pig pats at the agricultural shows, where these guiding sticks were inscribed with such wonderous designations as 'British Oil and Cake Mills', or Spillers Pig Feeds,' or 'Smiths Feed Supplements and Vitamins' emblazoned on the white painted woodwork. If the stockman parading the champion pig in the show-ring at the the agricultural show was using a particular company's pig pat he could be assured of getting half-a-crown from the feed company's local salesman.

"Roight," said Wilby, again, "goo an' git the pig pats, Tracy and git some string."

"Sharn't be a minitt," said Tracy, as she skipped off.

Wilby said, "Oi'll hev ta git the hammer back afore Dad come hom, do else Oi'll git wrong. I ent supposed ta hev it."

"It won't take more 'en ten minnits to make a cart," said Mort.

*   *   *   *

The building of the cart had proved to be more difficult and time consuming than they had previously thought and nearly two hours later they had tied the tea chest onto the two pram axles with string and they had knocked a dozen, three inch nails into the side of the tea chest to fix the shafts. In fact, the tea chest was having a bad time and the nails had caused some of the woodwork to split.

They now made preparations to furbish the cart with special attachments. The main distinctive, luxury fitting consisted of an odd piece of red carpet that Wilby had found in the bottom of his mother's kitchen cupboard. The piece of carpet was cut into shape with the aid of an old pair of rusty sheep shears that Mort had found hung up on a nail in the stable. The piece of carpet was then laid reverently on the floor of the cart.

In various areas of the cart floor and sides, the points of three inch nails raised their sharp ends and Wilby's efforts to hit them down with the hammer had only met with limited success. A registration number of WMIOO was carefully inscribed on the back with a piece of chalk, and an old bicycle bell was fixed to the offside of the cart with a piece of rusty bale-wire.

*   *   *   *

While Wilby and Mort were building their cart in the cartshed, two important characters in our story were in the tap room at the 'Dog and Duck'. They were Seymour Horncastle and Harrison Quill, who were both in their seventies and, according to a local wag, were in the Summer of senility. However, Seymour and Harrison were certain sure in their own minds that they were worthy, pivotable products of the Village.

Harrison Quill was a retired schoolmaster and lived, on his own, in a small, neat bungalow at the far end of the Village. Mrs. Creamer, who cleaned the school, 'did' for him twice a week. He was a lean and studious-looking man with long, grey hair and gold-rimmed spectacles. He was M.A.(Cantab) Hons. and had taught Greek and Ancient History to unresponsive boys in the Lower Fifth at St. Philip's Grammar. Being a classicist and a pillar of significance and with his keen intellect he knew that rooted in scholarship he had refinement thrust upon him.

Harrison wore a natty, fore and aft, green hat with woodcock feather and he carried a silver-knobbed walking cane. Whenever possible he wore a red carnation in his button-hole and, in the flower of his days, had been credited as having been something of a ladies' man. Being M.A.(Cantab) Hons. he spoke loudly and frequently about 'rowing' and 'The Boat', and he frequently prefaced his remarks with "When I was at Cambridge". However, before going up to Cambridge he had been educated at one of the lesser public schools, where there was no river and no rowing but where the heinous and brutal game of soccer was played. It was unkindly said that Harrison couldn't row a dingy across a pond.

As far as football was concerned, it has to be said that, Harrison had never played, as his fond mother had persuaded the school doctor that Harrison was a delicate child with a rheumatic heart and, consequently, on games afternoons Harrison would play chess with the indisposed pupils in the sick-bay.

Harrison's crony, Seymour Bertram Horncastle was a retired country solicitor. He had a Roman nose and a high, narrow forehead. He had been the Senior Partner in Horncastle, Hipwood, Son and Trott. In recent years he tended to oversee the settlements and wills of some of his older and wealthier clients and he left the work of divorces and tricky litigation, concerning garden fences and neighbourly disputes, to his junior partners.

Seymour, although arrogant and pompous, possessed a certain loyal integrity to his older clients, many of whom had departed this life. He had been known sharply to reprimand some of the younger and greedy beneficiaries of legacies for their over-eager and grasping natures. He had been particularly severe on young Eddie Brooks, the idle and ineffectual bachelor son of wealthy, property speculator, Hayden Brooks. Eddie had endeavoured to persuade Seymour to prevail upon his father to alter his will, to the ultimate outrageous disadvantage of his hardworking, younger brother, Henry. Henry was a poorly paid researcher in Imperial College in London, he had a hardworking wife and four children, and was living on the edge of his means. Seymour had given Eddie certain uncomplicated advice and had shown him smartly to the door.

Seymour, however, had now mellowed in the Summer of his retirement and had not only helped, on legal issues, members of lower income groups in the Village, free of charge, but he had also had more time to reflect on his quest for the meaning of the Universe and matters concerning the fate of mankind.

Seymour, in his brown herringbone tweed jacket and fawn cardigan and full of philosophical assumptions, considered himself to be well-informed on all aspects of the Nation in its social, historical and, indeed, in its theological context and he could not conceive of anyone doubting that he was the possessor of a first class mind.

It had been Harrison's round and he had moved with stiff, pompous steps up to the anchorage of the alcohol. Rosie Briggs, the barmaid, a shameless little tart, leant her breasts over the bar. It was said that Rosie did whenever she could. "What can I do for you, Mr. Harrison?" asked Rosie, quite mischieviously. Harrison, who was endeavouring to steer his eyes from Rosie's cleavage, which was placed some eighteen inches from his nose, reluctantly knew that Rosie could do nothing for him but draw him two pints of Adnams best. The foaming ale was handed over in their special pewter tankards which had reposed on the shelf behind the bar.

*   *   *   *

By early afternoon Harrison and Seymour had removed themselves from the 'Dog and Duck' and, with slightly bent shoulders and heedful of the twinges of their stiffening joints, were carefully making their way along Highbarns Lane. They were well pleased with their morning discussions. They were filled with much condemnation and criticism of both sides of industry, the state of the arts and the deplorable neglect of social conscience by the Government.

As they idly strolled along, side by side, they were entering into a spirited and exhaustive scrutiny of the deplorable morals and habits of 'the young'. They were forced to conclude that the young, in general, and their attitude to their elders and betters was cause for unmitigated vexation.

"The young of today," Harrison said, "are disrespectful, ill-mannered and cosseted. Education," he said, gravely, "is in decline."

Both Seymour and Harrison, with ponderous head wagging, deplored the pit of intellectual squalor that reposed in the Village. They made patronising and disparaging remarks concerning the majority of the populace and peasantry listed in the Parochial Electoral Register.

The common, vulgar tradespeople of the district, ignorant and full of shallow prattle, drove these two masters and champions of abstract thought and intellectual reflection to sigh heavily with disapproval. But the main concern of both Harrison and Seymour was the attitude of the young, which they both found profoundly depressing.

"I find," said Harrison, poking the air with his stick, "that the young are impertinent and discourteous, and if this generation is the Old Country's future then to allow them the prevalent degree of freedom is monumental stupidity and an exercise in futility."

"They abide," said Seymour, with opinionated fervour, "in spiritual putrescence and slovenliness and have no respect for their betters." Seymour lit his pipe. The two cronies were heavy with apprehension.

"The young should be forked on the midden," said Harrison, thoughtlessly.

"Hullo," said Seymour, pointing his stick, "what's going on here?"

Harrison and Seymour had stumbled across Wilby and Mortimer busily constructing their carriage in the old, tiled cartshed beside the road.

Wilby was giving orders to Mortimer, "Hold the cart steady, Mort, while I knock another two niles in, git out of the way, Tracy."

"You wanna look owt what you're a doin'," said Mortimer. "You're cackhanded. You nearly hit moi fingers last toime." Mort drew his fingers back nervously as Wilby wielded the hammer.

"You're wuss than an owd woman," said Wilby, as he wildly aimed at a partly submerged nail head.

"You be careful," said Mortimer, "that nile is all bent, you'll hev to git it owt with the owd claw 'ammer."

*   *   *   *

The two pillars of the Parish were leaning on their sticks some twenty feet away.

"Now what," said Harrison, "are our two apple-cheeked, chubby cherubs contriving this morning?"

"I have no doubt," said Seymour, "that whatever is being manufactured will be for the greater good of the Nation and mankind."

"Would it be a moon capsule?" ventured Harrison. His eyes gleamed with intellectual pleasure.

Mortimer realised that they were under observation and whispered to Wilby, "We got cumpny."

"Silly owd sods," muttered Wilby to Mort, "what they a' watchin' us for?"

"Hain't got nuthin' better to do," said Mortimer, "lazy owd buggers."

Harrison said to Seymour, in an undertone, "As a Cambridge man it would be a matter of unalloyed gratification if our two young, rough carpenters built the Oxford boat!"

Seymour, who had a keen perception of his own cleverness, sniggered and said, "Particularly if the little fellow in the big cap was Cox!"

*   *   *   *

It was clear that Harrison and Seymour were thoroughly enjoying their pointed, unflattering and abusive dissertations and homilies. They fondly imagined that they were composing witty verbal contributions to some of the most sharp-witted and withering invectives of our time.

Wilby and Mort had sharp ears and overheard what was being said, and there was no doubt that aggravation was being generated.

"Silly owd farts," said Wilby.

"Keep yer voice down," whispered Mort. But it was too late and Harrison and Seymour had clearly heard.

"Don't be cheeky, young man," said Harrison, loudly.

But Wilby was impervious to fear and embarrassment. "Muzzy owd bugger," said Wilby, not looking up and talking to the cart.

"Young fella doesn't know his pecking order," said Seymour, incredulous of having heard aright.

Harrison was now bereft of his courteous manner and shook his stick at Wilby. "I'll tell your father of you," he said, firmly.

"Don't care," said Wilby, still talking to the cart and pumped full of rebellion.

"I mean it," said Harrison, reddening.

"Bugger off," said Wilby, defiantly. "You're a dodderun owd bastard and keep yer trap shut."

Harrison heard this with cold disbelief. Tolerance was under great strain and in a tone of impressive pomposity he said, "If you aren't careful, young man, I'll use this stick to warm your backside."

"Try it," said Wilby, with contempt, "an' Oi'll ponk yer on the hooter."

"Shut up," said Mort to Wilby, "do else you'll cop it."

Harrison could hardly contain himself and dabbed his forehead with his red silk handkerchief. He knew full well that if he hit Wilby, Wilby would put on his big act of being hurt and would writhe in false agony. He also feared the legendary wrath of Mrs. Gert Potts, Wilby's mother. Mrs. Gerty Potts made Wilby change his pants regular in case he got run over. She defended her young like a rageful tigress and cooked them apple crumble every Saturday.

Gert Potts had been known, with folded arms, to rant on at her neighbour, Mrs. Fennel, for three quarters of an hour, without pause for breath and the verbal battle could be heard all over the Village. Indeed she had once carried on at Alf for half an hour while still polishing the stair rods. Other times she would storm and stomp round the kitchen banging saucepans about.

Alf had said more than once, "Gert do floi orf the handle."

Perhaps one of Gert's most noteworthy victories was when the never, never man came to Mrs. Potts to collect the hire purchase payments. They reckoned that in his rush to get out of the gate and carrying his briefcase, and escape the displeasure of Gert Potts, the young man's feet never touched the ground.

"Come away, Harrison," urged Seymour, tugging at his sleeve.

So Harrison Quill, full of subliminal arrogance and the castigator of the young, trembling with wrath and indignation, lost stomach for further odious contravention.

Summoning up as much dignity as he could muster and shaking his silver-knobbed cane at Wilby, he finally turned away from the Field of Blood and Combat towards the comparative sanctuary of the main road.

When Harrison and Seymour had gone Wilby said, "Short-arsed gits, they put years on me."

"If Quilly comes much of that," said Mortimer, feeling brave for the first time, "I'll put a catapult through his winda."

Wilby said, "Mum says he's got the hide of a 'nocerous."

"What's a 'nocerous?" asked Mortimer.

Wilby ignored him.

*   *   *   *

Having divested themselves of Harrison and Seymour, the two young, project managers and masters of design stood back and contentedly surveyed the rough cut fruits of their industry.

"That's a helluppin good cart, innit?" said Wilby, happily inspecting the cart from all angles.

"Dun't know sa much," said Mort, apprehensively, "got sev'ral niles stickin' up fru the floor."

"Niles is too long," said Wilby. "Shouldn't ought to knock three inch niles into half inch board."

"Hope the shafts dun't come orf, then," said Mort.

"Dun't be an owd worry guts," said Wilby. "Leave the bell alone, Tracy."

"Now," announced Wilby, "we're ready to hev a goo. Git in the cart, Mort and Oi'll give ya a roide down the hill."

"Let Tracy hev a roide fust," said Mortimer, whose iron nerves were faltering in the emotional melodrama and the excitement of it all.

"Shan't," said Tracy, "wheels moight come orf."

"Tain't sa loikely," said Mort, regaining his lost courage, "Oi'll git in, then."

Mort gingerly climbed into the cart and sat down on the piece of red carpet on the floor while Wilby held onto the shafts. "Dun't goo too fast then," said Mort, urgently.

Wilby pushed the cart out onto the short, steep hill which led down to the bottom of the farmyard.

Mort hung onto the sides of the cart, and in a fit of bravado he banged away at the sides of the cart, rang the bicycle bell and shouted, "Herrip. Herrip. Herrip. Here we come. Herrip."

Tracy was very impressed and squealed with admiration. She stood on her toes and waved her little pink handkerchief.

"Here we come, then," shouted Wilby, gripping the two shafts and breaking into a fast trot and pushing the cart with gathering speed down the hill.

"Steady up," shouted Mort, "there ain't no hurry. Steady up."

But events were rapidly edging away from Wilby's immediate ability to change gear and, in spite of attempts to slow down, the weight of Mortimer and the steepness of the hill ensured that considerable momentum was being generated. The whole stirring issue was beginning to get out of control and Wilby was impelled to run faster and faster.

"Starp!" shouted Mort, "Starp!"

The indications were that proceedings were heading for early disaster and that casualties were imminent. Wilby quickly developed a pother of enthusiasm for self-preservation. It was clear that Mort and the cart were about to part company and, sensing calamity, Wilby let go of the shafts.

The rudderless cart, with the terrified Mort aboard, now in the throws of a major technical malfunction, was gathering speed as it tore away down the hill.

At the bottom of the hill the cart, which had a mind of its own, collided with a large brick and the rear offside wheel came off and shot into an extensive patch of nettles growing round two half-filled drums of creosote.

As in many East Englian farmyards, at the very bottom of the hill there was a mucky, green weeded pond which also did service as a cesspit for the cowshed and the stables.

When the wheel came off and flew into the nettles the offside shaft broke in two and anyone could see that imminent disaster was about to strike the whole flipping' shebang. It was clear that Mort was heading for an early and spectacular displacement of mud, cesspit sludge and dredgy bilge water.

*   *   *   *

It would be untrue to say that Mort flew out of the cart, but Mort had always boasted to his school friends that when he grew up he was going to be a Spitfire pilot and he had a picture over his bed of Sir Douglas Bader, the legless fighter ace, gunning down an intruding Dornier over the coast of Kent. Here was Mort, to all intents and purposes, experiencing the nearest sensation he ever would have of a Spitfire over the English Channel, in the Battle of Britain, heading for the drink.

It took the best part of three seconds in uncontrolled and unco-ordinated curved flight for the airborne Mort to hit the turgid pond of slush and slime in a resounding splash.

*   *   *   *

Wilby was certain that Mort would be killed and Tracy was screaming blue murder. Tracy, however, believed in God and Jesus and prayed very, very hard that Mort would go to Heaven.

The pond, however, was very shallow and was covered in green weeds and gummy forms of algae. There were no fish in the pond but Wilby and Mort had been known to fish for sharks, using a bent pin and a thatching peg, to scare Tracy.

When Mortimer hit the surface the dross displacement and the surging cascade of reeking muckiness made the frogspawn in the corner of the pond distinctly wobble.

After four seconds, Mort, like a depth-charged U-Boat, surfaced. He had struggled to his feet and stood in the pond with his head and hair covered in green weed and mud. Slime was running down his face and his flat cap was floating away like the Kontiki. Mortimer, added grief to his sorrow by yelling his head off.

"Shut up, Mort," shouted Wilby. "Bader wouldn't make all that row droppin' in the drink."

"I'm soppin' wet," cried Mortimer, holding up his arms in dejected misery.

Wilby picked up the broken shaft of the cart and, holding onto one end, poked the other end to Mortimer, "Grab hold o' this."

And Mortimer gratefully caught hold of the end and Wilby hauled him out. Mortimer, wringing wet in a soaking, crumpled, grey jersey and green weed and slime in his hair and on his clothes looked like a bedraggled bloodhound that had just come through the sheep dip. Garlanded with a wreath of dripping twigs and leaves on his head, he could have been the Son of Ceasar.

"Cor," said Wilby, "Mort, you don't half stink."

Somehow Mortimer had managed to collect a short piece of thornbush which was sticking on the back of his short trousers. Tracy feared the worst and yelled, "Cor, look at Mort, ee's gotta nile in his bum."

*   *   *   *

Alf Potts, Wilby's father, and Bert Hick, part-time dayman, were driving the Gloucester Old Spot Boar up to the sow service pens. Alf and Bert, who claimed to have once seen Princess Margaret, were none too pleased as the two pig pats that they had always used to drive the boar, were nowhere to be found. The boar was a

fully pedigree animal and was registered with the Gloucester Old Spot Pedigree
Pig Society, as Newton Hall Grand Duke 123rd, but Alf always called the boar
'Olly' after Oliver Hardy.

Olly was always taken up to the sows service area twenty one days after the first
service to make sure than none of the sows had 'come over' and hadn't 'took'. Alf
knew that an old sow was 'on' for three days and he found that to get the old sow
to get 'took' was to get Olly to catch her on the third day 'just afore she goo orf'.
To tell you the truth old Olly didn't want much driving up to the sow pens – he
knew his way all right and usually at least one of the sows was glad to see him. So
on the way up to the service area Olly usually led Alf and Bert by about fourteen
lengths.

Alf and Bert heard the commotion down by the pond and Alf broke off to see
what all the row was about. Mortimer and Tracy were still yelling their heads off.

Alf nearly always, and not without reason, blamed his son Wilby for everything.
"Wot you bin up to, yew young perisher," said Alf menacingly.

"Wheel come orf," said Wilby.

"Oi'll give yew, wheel come orf," said Alf, undoing his leather belt, "an' wot
yew bin a' doin' wiv moi 'ammer? If yew ain't careful, you'll git a fourpenny one."

Alf often threatened his son but Wilby knew that his father wouldn't give him a
leathering – he never did and Mrs Potts had been known to say that Alf had taken
his belt off to his son as many as six times during a weekend. Alf would say, "Oi'd
giv 'im a clip round the ear only Oi 'ad me 'ans in me pocket."

Mortimer was shivering with the cold and Wilby started to wipe him down with
handfuls of barley straw and an old meal bag. Alf then rose to the full height of his
limited authority and said, "Tracy, you goo home and Wilby yew take Mort back

to the Vicarage and make sure the parson dun't see yer, do else all hell'ul be let loose."

So Wilby, full of concern, accompanied the half-drowned and miserable Mortimer back to his home at the Vicarage and had hoped to slide off home the moment the Vicarage back door came in sight. But Mrs. Trussel had seen the furtive Wilby and her bedraggled son climb through the garden fence. Mrs. Trussel ordered Mortimer to take off all his clothes and leave them outside the back door while she ran the bath and, as Wilby related afterwards, "She never asked me in fer lemonade or nothun'".

When Wilby arrived home, some ten minutes later, Mrs. Potts had already got out the round tin bath and was heating up the hot water in the copper and when the clean and soapy-smelling Wilby arrived in the kitchen, after his bath, he had two large slices of bread and dripping. Tracy, who had had her knickers changed for the second time in the past hour, had a sticky bun and three helpings of jelly.

That night Wilby, after he had pushed the pot back under the bed, schemed as to how to make a boat out of the old discarded potato riddle, and then he thought long and hard about the stirring events of the day. Eventually, he had decided that Mort had proved to be no great shakes in helping to make the cart and, moreover than that, he had sat in the cart lopsided. Eventually he said aloud to himself and his teddy , "I shouldn't never hev let him went."

CHAPTER EIGHTEEN
Interval in the Laundry

I had been busy since eight o'clock doing the unpleasant, smelly job of dagging the ewes, there had been a bit of fly strike. It was 10.30am and I had just come into the kitchen for a mid-morning cup of coffee. I had drained the cup, rinsed it under the tap and set it down by the sink, and then went upstairs to change. The Bank Manager held lunches in the Directors' Room at the Bank for about six people, and I was invited two or three times a year. I always enjoyed these lunches as I would often be the only farmer present and it was interesting to meet directors of some of the local companies and sometimes the owners of shops in the High Street.

Julie was ironing my shirts in the laundry room. I opened my sock drawer in the bedroom and shouted down the stairs, "Julie, why is it that I put three pairs of socks in the dirty washing basket and when I get them back, they are five odd ones? There are not even two socks of the same colour."

I went downstairs and dumped the five odd socks on the draining board.

"Your best bet," said Julie, "is just to buy black ones from Marks and Sparks and what is more you are an old fusspot, and I wish you'd empty your pockets before you put things in the wash and that you wouldn't leave your washing on the floor with the shirt inside the jumper and both inside out. And another thing," went on Julie, "it's high time you bought me a washing machine."

"I thought you'd got one," I said.

"Typical," said Julie, "that's absolutely typical. You notice that your socks don't match up, but you don't notice that I haven't got a washing machine like all the other farmers' wives round here."

"I can't see that a washing machine is going to make my socks match up," I said. "How much will a washing machine cost?"

"Two hundred and fifty pounds," said Julie.

"Good Lord," I said, "we can't run to that, I can buy a good second-hand muck spreader for that."

"Typical again," said Julie, "you will spend thousands on tractors and combines and I have to put up with this antiquated boiler."

"It's electric isn't it?" I said.

"Electric, my foot," said Julie, "the water is heated by electricity but then I have all the work to do."

"Right," I said, "I'll have to think about getting you a new washing machine."

"You'll do nothing of the sort," said Julie, firmly, "now that we have got this far you'll go into Middlesham tomorrow morning and order one. I'll see what '*Which*' is saying about washing machines and let you know what make to order."

"I don't know," I said, "all I said was that I had five socks back from the wash that didn't match and I end up by being sent off to spend money on a washing machine that we don't need and can't afford."

"Nonsense," said Julie, "in another two years, at this rate, we will have paid off our overdraft, and we will be the owners of eight hundred and fifty acres of farm land, three farmhouses, eight cottages, altogether worth a couple of million."

"I don't know, Julie," I said, "you're getting to be a real overbearing, know-all, bossy boots."

"I'll give you bossy boots," said Julie, picking up a wet tea cloth. It was flung with great accuracy and hit me in the back of the neck.

"Right," I said, "now you're in big trouble, you've really done it this time."

Julie made a dash for the door but I was there first and when I caught her I picked her up under my arm and turned her upside down and said, "Now I'm going to stick your head in the boiler." Julie only weighed eight and a half stone and the sacks of clover seed that we carried in the barn weighed eighteen stone, so she was like a feather.

Julie, her legs kicking the air and hair all over the place, was putting on a great act of being murdered.

I held her upside down over the bubbling boiler and said, "Is there anything you wish to say before I drop you in?"

Julie was still screaming and just at that moment Sally Henderson walked in. "Don't mind me," said Sally, "why are you trying to kill Julie, Albert?"

"She sent me back five odd socks from the wash," I said.

"Put me down," yelled Julie.

"Shall I?" I asked Sally.

"Well, that's up to you," said Sally, "but if you can hold her upside down till Peter comes in, he'll see all she's got and I won't be able to do anything with him."

"Put me down," screamed Julie, again, "or I'll kill you."

"I think," said Sally, "as there seems to be a lot of killing going on, and as I don't particularly wish to be the witness to one or even two murders, I'd better pop into the kitchen and put the coffee on."

When I put Julie down, she started to comb her hair and she said coolly, and with a toss of her head, "I'm going to leave you, Albert, and go home to Mum."

"Don't forget to leave a message on the bathroom mirror," I said.

"I'm glad I hit you on the back of the neck with a wet towel."

"You may have won the first round," I said, "but I reckon I won the replay."

The next morning, while having breakfast in the kitchen, Julie said to me sharply, "Don't be sluttish, using your knife to scoop out the marmalade."

"There's no spoon," I said.

"There's one in the drawer," said Julie.

"I bet that Prince Philip doesn't have all this bother," I said. "Anyway, it is a clean knife."

"Prince Philip knows better than you not to use a knife on the marmalade pot," said Julie.

The phone rang. "I bet it's Sally," I said.

"You go," said Julie.

"No. You go. It won't be for me."

It was Sally, all right and then it was natter, natter, natter. The principal reason for the phone call was for Sally and Julie to decide what to wear at the forthcoming High Sheriff's Garden Party.

"Is it hats?" asked Sally.

"Of course," replied Julie.

"I shall have to get something new," said Sally.

"I think I'll make do with the pink and white that I had for the first day of the Show," said Julie.

"That'll be nice," said Sally.

I opened the door and came into the hall. The light was streaming through the mullioned windows.

"Hurry up," I said, "I want to phone the beet factory."

"Won't be a minute," said Julie, pulling up a chair.

"Who is that?" enquired Sally.

"Only my husband," said Julie.

"Give him my love," said Sally, brightly, "has he tried to stick your head in the boiler again?"

"I hope you haven't mentioned that to anyone," said Julie, anxiously.

"Well I only mentioned it to a few of the ladies at the W.I. Committee meeting," said Sally, mischievously, "and they promised not to let it go any further."

"I'll kill you," said Julie.

"Tell Sally," I said, "to wear skin-tight leopard skin drainpipes and a red and blue bikini at the High Sheriff's Garden Party."

"I heard that," said Sally, "and tell Albert to wear wellingtons and a pair of blinkers."

"What no fig leaves?" said Julie.

"Good gracious, no. Fig leaves would be quite unnecessary and Mrs. Dimbleby-Farquarson would be so disappointed!"

"Hurry up with the phone," I said. "Why do you always have to phone each other, and get engaged in this trivial and twadling shallow prattle, between nine and ten in the morning when I nearly always want to use the phone?"

"Shush," said Julie, "Did you get the wheel changed on my car?"

"No, I didn't," I said, "you've got a wheel brace and a jack in the boot of your car, I don't know why you haven't changed it yourself. The Queen was in the ATS during the war and she can change a wheel."

"That was before she had a husband to help her," said Julie.

"I've got to run over to Ipswich to get a new set of nozzles for the sprayer and I won't be in for lunch until a quarter to one."

"I'll leave your lunch," said Julie, "there's a bit of cold beef in the fridge, and I'll leave some carrots in the side oven. You'll need to put the potatoes on the ring for five minutes, and there's a strawberry yoghurt in the fridge and while you're in Ipswich see if there is anything you would like for your supper."

"I want supper to be a surprise," I said, "and ask Sally if I can go over there for lunch."

"No good doing that," said Julie, "you know they say that if you can't stand the heat, get out of the kitchen, so Sally and I are going over to Sudbury to buy a new hat."

"It looks as though Peter and I aren't going to get any lunch," I said, peevishly.

"If you are too busy or too idle to take your lunch out of the oven," said Julie, "why don't you two money-bags take yourselves off to the 'Little Chef'. Ted's youngest daughter works there and she will look after you and I'll pay for both of you, if you like."

CHAPTER NINETEEN
The Pig Unit

Julie said to me, "You know, Albert, our pigs have done very well for us since the War and we have got our breeding and management policies down to a reasonably fine art. In fact, the improvement in our pig herd's performance has been spectacular. By testing and recording we have succeeded in producing quick-growing pigs with plenty of lean meat and, most important of all, with a good conversion of feed into meat."

Julie said, "I think that we ought to expand the pig unit to four hundred sows and run all the progeny through to bacon weight."

"I am all for that," I said, "and, if all went well, we should with 2.2 litters per sow, per year, be selling eight thousand pigs a year."

"I am not letting you keep the sows in tethers or in individual sow stalls," said Julie.

"Don't worry," I said, "the sows would be kept in straw yards in batches of twenty, like we do now. We knew that when you put a lot of sows together you get a tremendous lot of fighting and bullying, and the bigger sows will dominate the smaller ones until a pecking order is established and unless we feed the sows in individual feeders the sows at the bottom of the pecking order will be kept away from the feeding troughs."

"I think that if I was a sow that I should prefer to take a chance in a yard of bullying sows than to be stuck in a stall where I couldn't turn round," said Julie. "What should we want in the way of additional housing?"

"First of all, we should have to build a new farrowing house with maternity quarters for another fifty sows and litters.
Each of the farrowing pens would require creeps so that the little pigs don't get laid on by their mothers and there would have to be at least two infra-red lamps in each pen to keep the piglets warm. The farrowing house would cost as much as two Jaguar cars, and if we borrow a lot of money and this little enterprise went up the wall we might have to learn to ride a second hand bike."

"What else should we want?" said Julie.

"The extension to our 'carry on' pens, where the piglets go after being weaned would set us back another Jag. but the main expense would be in building a fattening house to hold two thousand pigs, and it would require the value of three Rolls Royces to pay for that. If we are going to build a brand new fattening house we might as well make sure that we have the latest in design so you and I had better prepare for a grand tour to look at the latest in pig housing."

During the next four weeks Julie and I visited seven large pig units in Yorkshire and Scotland, two in Belgium and one in Denmark. By the end of our tour we were

clear in our minds on the type of fattening house that we should require and also
the type of machinery and fittings which would have to be installed.

The fattening house would be three hundred and forty feet long and one
hundred and sixty feet wide. It would have warm, straw-lined kennels for sleeping
quarters and the pigs would be kept in batches of fifteen in each pen. They would
be automatically fed, twice a day, by a time clock system. There would be an
elaborate control panel with micro-processors accurately to measure the amounts
of feed and water dispensed into each of the pen troughs. The roof of the building
would use a hundred tons of asbestos.

There would be discussions with the Electricity Board because they would be
required to install larger cables and the Water Board would be laying larger bore
piping to cope with the extra five thousand gallons of water which would be used
every day.

I did a deal with the bank on overdraft and they agreed that we should pay one
and a half per cent interest over base rate. If we were 'on the ball' and everything
went well, the budget indicated that with profits from our corn and poultry we
should be able to pay off the overdraft in two to three years.

CHAPTER TWENTY
The High Sheriff's Garden Party

The High Sheriff's Garden Party, held in high summer, was one of the highlights of the County Social year. It took place in late July and invitations arrived five weeks beforehand. The grand party with champagne, large marquees, daintily cut sandwiches, canapes, delicious delicate cakes and pastries, according to Wilfred, cost the High Sheriff an arm and a leg.

Julie and I, therefore, were delighted to receive a large, stiff envelope with 'From the office of the High Sheriff' imprinted on the back and the embossed gold lettered card with our invitation. We never knew quite why we were invited but somehow we had been put on 'the list'.

The County Sheriff for the year was Colonel Dimbleby Farquarson, a tall, upright soldier with grey hair and a military moustache. He stood 6ft 3ins and was credited with being one of the best shots in East Anglia.

The Dimbleby Farquarsons had a sporting lodge in Scotland where there was hind shooting at Christmas. At Easter they would be up for some early salmon and trout fishing and later on, in August, the grouse and a bit of stalking. The High Sheriff, who was always well turned out and something of a snappy dresser obtained his suits from Anderson and Sheppard. He had married his wife, Phillipa – Boo Boo to her friends – just after the War. She was the daughter of Sir Richard Savendale, an extremely wealthy entrepreneur, who bought companies and sold off the assets.

*　　　*　　　*　　　*

Phillipa Farquarson, a tall stately woman, had had a tiresome morning. Her precocious eleven year old son, Crispin, now on school holidays, had been asking awkward questions at breakfast. "How, Mother, do you move from the middle class to the upper class?" he said.

"One can't," said his mother, firmly.

"Not even if you win the pools?"

"Certainly not. To win the pools could condemn one for life – it is a form of low class gambling."

"But Daddy gambles on the stock exchange and on property developments."

"That's different."

"But surely all the upper class are rich like us."

"It does help to be rich but class had nothing to do with money."

"What does it have to do with then?" persisted Crispin.

"Well," said his mother, "there are two things which are important. One is the ownership of land and the other concerns where you went to school."

"So, no upper class people come from Grammar schools?" said Crispin.

"Very few indeed. The best people have all been to an expensive Public School. You will find that your friends at Eton will be friends for life. They will help you into good positions in the City. Later on you will find that they know all about non-executive directorships, how to make a great deal of money and how to avoid paying Income Tax and Estate Duty."

"The people who own the land are not farmers then?"

"Good gracious, no," said his mother, "the upper class do not farm their land. They let it to tenant farmers and many of the big landowners are pulling in over a quarter of a million a year from rents."

"I expect that we are considered snobs by the local people not like us?"

"That is possible, dear, but, in fact, many of the middle class are more snobbish than we are but the trouble with many of them is that they have got money but very little culture."

"Like the oikes from the Council Estate."

"You are not to call them that, Crispin."

"Mr. Haseldene, our Chemistry Master, is an oike and hasn't got any culture," volunteered Crispin.

"Why do you say that?" asked his mother.

"He farts during lessons," said Crispin.

"Do not use that awful word," said his mother.

*   *   *   *

When Julie and I arrived at the gates of the High Sheriff's residence we joined a queue of cars which was directed by the Police and two NCOs, from the local Territorial Unit, to the car park in the field behind the ha-ha. The five acre meadow had been cut with gang mowers and manicured like a lawn. I went round and opened the car door for Julie and she stepped out onto the mown grass. In her new outfit which she had purchased from a fashion shop in Sudbury, she was a picture. "If the *Tatler* people ask me what are you wearing, what am I to tell them?" I said, mischieviously.

"You can tell them," said Julie, "that I am wearing a floral pink suit with pointed pepham hemline, puff shoulders and a straight skirt."

"And what about the hat?" I said.

"You can tell the reporters and fashion writers, who will be swarming round you asking what I am wearing, that I am wearing a 'back of the head' Breton hat in the same fabric as my suit."

"And what will you say that I am wearing?" I said.

"I shall tell them," said Julie, "the truth. That you are wearing a lightweight, off the peg, dark pin stripe suit from Marks and Sparks and that it cost you the best part of seventy quid."

"Eighty quid, actually," I said, "and they told me that I could change it if it was too tight round the middle."

"I think you'd better have a word with Weightwatchers," said Julie, "You are beginning to put on a bit of tummy."

"I am certainly not," I said, patting my middle jacket button, "this very slight protrusion is muscle.

Our kind hosts welcomed us under a pink and white awning at the main garden entrance in front of the very impressive Tudor residence which was fashioned in oak timbers and embattled brick. The rose coloured bricks on the magnificent octagonal chimneys glowed richly in the afternoon sun.

The High Sheriff had been in a somewhat unhappy mood as his eldest son, Piers, had pranged the Bentley when returning, in the early hours, from the Hunt Midsummer Ball. He was also miffed that his usually reliable City contact had failed to get him an invitation to the Members' Stand for the forthcoming Test Match at Lords. However, the beautiful day and limitless homage had brightened him up and, in welcoming Julie, he said, "What have you got for the Point to Points next season, Mrs. Cooper?"

"I'm getting a bit old for racing now," said Julie. "My Irish horse has got another year in him and I shall probably ride him at Cottenham."

"I always put a saver on you when you are riding," said the High Sheriff.

"That's very kind of you to say so," said Julie.

Standing beside the High Sheriff, Phillipa Dimbleby Farquarson appeared rather ill at ease. She was a prey to worry. She had worried about the weather and the caterers and her hat and her special leading role on this prestigious County occasion. She extended a brief, cool hand and gently touched the triple row of pearls nestling in the pink chiffon scarf at her throat.

We passed through the gate and the terrace, where champagne was being served deferentially by the County Caterers. Carrying our glasses, we moved on through the Victorian topiary garden and under the climbing plants of the pagoda and out onto the crowded lawn. Here there were various gentlefolk, near gentlefolk and respected members of the Squirearchy.

Standing by the pool, chatting to Fiona Buck, the authoress, was Sir Horace Cope, of Addenbrookes and Guys, who, for two thousand pounds, had recently stitched up the High Sheriff's hernia.

The guests were a cross-section of the strata of the County. There were Mayors of the Boroughs, in their limousines, with their wives and gleaming chains of office. The Lord Lieutenant and his wife were there talking to the Chief Constable. A sizeable clutch of Deputy Lieutenants and a couple of MEPs, hoping for more power to the European Parliament in Brussels. Past Chairmen of the County Council, still on committees and still making regular visits to County Hall. Gillian Smart, the second wife of the immediate past Chairman of the Magistrates, was pretty, clever and dark eyed and when I said, "You know, Julie, that girl could go places."

Julie said, "If you don't take your lecherous eyes off her, you'll be going places!"

A couple of Bishops, with champagne in one hand and a sausage roll in the other, were worriedly discussing the inability of parishes to sustain and shoulder their diocesan quotas. There was a sprinkling of T.A. Colonels and Lord Rockwood, an aged Knight of the Shires was there. His Lordship, was often to be seen in Middlesham wearing old flannel bags and a threadbare jacket with scuffed leather elbows.

Sir William Pool was there in deep discussion with Francis Trotter, a distinguished Civil Servant of the Board of Trade. Sir William, who had had three wives, was head of a conglomerate that owned gold and diamond mines in Africa. His company managed ranches in Argentina and tens of thousands of arid acres in Australia's North West Territories. In the good years the millions rolled in but there was always the risk of rebellion and strikes in the mines in Africa and in the vast farm ranges in periods of drought, the sheep and cattle could die in their thousands. There was the manipulation of the prices of copper and coffee which could sink to the bottom line. I remember that Sally once said that she would love to be a tycoon and when I asked her why, she said, "The great advantage is, it makes people grovel."

Over by the orangery there was the loud voice with an expensive public school accent endeavouring to combat the prejudices of his inferiors.

*   *   *   *

I often found on these occasions that I was sometimes a back number as it was clear that Julie, wherever she went, was held in high regard. She had become well-known throughout East Anglia as a very good and brave steeplechase jockey and many people at the Garden Party had seen her, two nights previously, on television with two nationally known event riders doing a dressage demonstration at Stoneleigh.

However, I was now a J.P. and Chairman of the South of England Agricultural Advisory Panel and Chairman of the Committee which ran the Ministry Experimental Husbandry Station at Middle Easton. This had all resulted in Julie and I being invited to a Garden Party at Buckingham Palace where we had stood around with about a thousand other people eating cream cakes and strawberries served by the Joe Lyons catering staff.

*   *   *   *

However, here we were at a great County event far away from Buckingham Palace enjoying the hospitality of our hosts. The refreshments would be every bit as delicious as those dispensed in the tea marquee at the Palace.

The West Suffolk Yeomanry Band was playing under the enormous Cedar tree, which was casting long shadows over the middle of the immaculate lawn.

At six o'clock I said to Julie, "We've been here nearly a couple of hours, I think we ought to be on our way."

"O.K." said Julie, who was heavily involved in a discussion with Vic Silvers, who was training at Newmarket. "We must say goodbye to our hosts."

On the way home in the car I said to Julie, "You know, I always dread coming to these parties but when I am there I really enjoy them."

"So do I," said Julie, removing her hat and throwing it onto the back seat.

"What," I asked, "were you and Vic Silvers in deep discussion about?"

"Oh," said Julie, "he wondered if I would ride one of his horses in the Newmarket Plate."

"Isn't that the race for lady jockeys?" I said.

"Yes," said Julie.

"And doesn't Princess Anne ride in that race?"

"She has done," said Julie.

When we arrived home Julie said, "Do you want the bath?"

"No," I said, "I'll use the shower."

Back at the scene of the Garden Party, the Caterers had now packed up and gone home and the High Sheriff had climbed the stairs to his dressing room. Here he had removed his well cut suit and loosened the tight collar round his neck. He then flung his shirt, pants and socks into the soiled linen basket, and walked naked across the landing to the blue bathroom carrying a clean shirt, pants and his pocket radio. It had been a great day, the weather was perfect and the gardens were at their best. The High Sheriff would now relax in the Victorian, six foot, iron bath and while he leisurely soaked and took his ease he would listen to the City prices and the 7 o'clock news.

Over in the en suite bathroom his wife had kicked off her shoes into the corner and dropped her clothes on the floor. Her feet were hot and tired as she had been standing all the afternoon. As she sank into the steaming bath she grabbed the enormous sponge and luxuriated in the delicate smell of the scented soap and the fragrance of the bath salts.

It had been a grand day and one for which they had been planning for nearly a year.

*   *   *   *

Crispin, on the other hand, had taken his four ten out of the gun cupboard and was now in the garden trying to get a rabbit.

CHAPTER TWENTY-ONE

The Bull

It was a quiet September morning. The corn harvest was over and root harvesting and bale carting were in full swing and I was working in the office, planning the cropping programme for the next year. The phone rang. It was Peter to tell me that Andrew Moffit's Friesian bull had broken out of his pen and was running wild. No bull can be trusted and we knew that Andrew's bull had violence in his flesh and was extremely dangerous. Two weeks earlier, in his fierce anger, he had nearly killed Will Jepson, Andrew's head cowman, who had been pinned against the wall. Will was still in hospital. The beast could sometimes be heard roaring in his pen from over a mile away.

Because the bull was so dangerous Andrew had threatened to get rid of him. The bull, however, had sired very high yielding heifers, some of them giving over two thousand gallons with their first calf. The bull was five years old, treacherous and as strong as a tank.

The police had been informed and Andrew, who was nearly sixty, agreed that, as the bull was so dangerous, it would have to be shot. I knew Inspector Colin Barnes of the West Suffolk Police and he was aware that Peter and I had .303 rifles and that we both had a licence to cull deer. He also knew that as ex-soldiers we would know which end the bullets came out. The Inspector wondered if Peter and I could go out with the police as they had none of their marksmen available.

*　　　*　　　*　　　*

Peter drove over in his Land Rover and the police had their own four wheel drive vehicle. When I went into the gun room for my rifle Julie, who was ironing shirts in the kitchen, just said, "Albert, do be careful."

One of Andrew Moffit's tractor drivers had just driven over in his van to tell us that the bull was in Thorley Wood, and that he had been roaring and pawing the ground and didn't seem too happy.

I climbed in beside Peter and while he drove, I loaded five rounds in each of the magazines and put them on the ledge behind the windscreen. I held onto the rifles with their butts on the floor. The police vehicle followed closely behind.

When we reached the edge of the wood the great hoofmarks could be clearly seen where the bull had forced his way into the undergrowth. The wood was dense and there was no way of getting the Land Rover into the wood. The young constable, who had the rifle, was looking distinctly nervous, and Peter and I decided that it would be better and safer if he kept out of the way while we followed the great hoofmarks into the boscage and thicket.

We were both wearing our green Barbour shooting jackets and thornproof trousers. I handed Peter his rifle and a clip of five rounds. We stopped at the track where the footprints entered the wood and listened for any sign of the bull. There was only a mute, deathlike eerie stillness. With magazines fixed and safety catches on we pushed our way into the dense undergrowth and under the great canopy of woodbine. The wood stank of dank rotting leaves. Some disturbed wood pigeons were circling above and in the far distance a cock pheasant was 'cock cocking' as he flew out at the far end of the wood. We were following the bull's spoor – it was dark and eerie and a sudden cold dampness seemed to descend from the canopy above.

The bull had pushed through a drainage ditch which was half full of leaves and black stagnant water. The water nearly came to the top of our rubbers. We scrambled up the slippery bank and stood by a dead oak tree which was covered in ivy and creeper like a contorted reptile of the ancient world.

"Listen", said Peter, quietly, as a cold draught of air blew into our faces. But again the wood was as quiet as the grave.

The spoors were easy to follow through the soft mud where the great beast had smashed through the creeper and twisted brushwood. We somehow sensed that we were getting closer to the bull and moved forward with great caution.

After pushing forward another twenty paces we came to a clearing which had recently been coppiced and the sprouted growth had been cut from the sheared stumps. The clearing was about forty yards across and Peter tapped me on the shoulder and pointed to a black thicket on the other side of the clearing. "That's him," said Peter, in a whisper.

It was just possible to discern the great mass and shape of the bull. He was facing us and was standing there motionless and half hidden in the undergrowth. We knew he was watching us.

The bull had now pushed forward, corrupt, evil and massive. He began to paw the earth and it was clear that there was vengeance in his heart and hatred and anger seethed in him. He hardened his neck, and his massive head was swinging from side to side and his tail swished in savage fury. There was wrath and rage, like an iron furnace, foaming in his blood. The bull lowered his huge head and, still pawing the ground, gathered his great muscles. Peter and I dropped onto one knee, pushed one up the spout and clicked the bolt on our rifles. We were about six yards apart.

"Now, Peter," I said.

But before we could take aim the bull had burst out of the thicket and charged. Lashed into fury, the brute poured out the vials of his wrath. He came fast with blazing eyes in his killing rage. Peter and I fired as one, and the .303 bullets cracked into his boiling flesh. A fountain of blood erupted from his neck, and he momentarily checked, and, in his festering hatred, resumed his savage thrust. We had both done sharp shooting on the ranges and got two more into him. The wounded beast was within fifteen yards of Peter, and as he reeled, blundered and lunged towards Peter he gave a great wild bellow, like a madman's song. The .303 rounds, however, had found their mark. With a fountain of blood gushing from his neck the wounded beast sank to his knees. With a scream of pain and anger the bull keeled over and groaned in the wild throws of death, not five yards from where Peter was kneeling with his rifle.

The bull was still not quite dead and was kicking and flailing with his legs in the air and was hissing blood. I walked over to him and shot him in the heart.

I was not elated at what we had done but, as in the War, we had done what had to be done.

"You all right, Peter?"

"Yes," said Peter, "but if the bastard could have stayed on his feet for another three seconds he would have been on top of me."

We heard people approaching through the undergrowth and they soon came into view. They were led by Inspector Barnes and followed by the young constable. Behind were Andrew Moffit and Julie.

Julie took one look at the dead beast, rushed over to me and flung herself into my arms. She didn't say a word but the tears were streaming down her face.

CHAPTER TWENTY-TWO
The Visit of the President

Our NFU County Chairman was Gordon Shottsford, and he 'phoned me in early March. He said that arrangements were being made for Sir Henry Plumb, the President of the National Farmers' Union, to visit the County in July. Sir Henry would be taken round some of the local farms in the morning, and he had agreed to address a large gathering of farmers, from all over East Anglia, in the afternoon.

Gordon asked if Julie and I would have any objection to the afternoon meeting being held in our new corn store. Julie and I regarded this as a compliment indeed.

The store itself was two hundred and forty feet long and one hundred and twenty feet wide and had only been in use for one harvest. The building was rather stark and austere with a concrete floor and an asbestos roof, and it would hold almost two thousand tons of wheat. Underneath the floor there were air ducts for blowing hot air through the grain, and drying it all down to fifteen per cent moisture at which level the grain would keep until the New Year. At one end there hung two enormous sliding doors where the merchants' lorries would stand to be filled from the five ton bucket on our four-wheel drive fork lift truck.

*   *   *   *

It was a hot July day and the crops all over the Eastern Counties were looking well and full of promise. The winter barleys were beginning to turn. It was a quiet time on the arable farms of East Anglia and the harvest was two or three weeks away.

We had been told to expect between four hundred and five hundred farmers at the meeting, which was billed as 'an open day'. This indicated that visitors were welcome to look round the farm if they so wished.

The corn store had been emptied in March and it had been vacuumed and fumigated ready for harvest. We had put out four hundred bales of straw for seats, and Happy Tattersall had pulled into the store an old wooden farm waggon for the platform party.

I had cut and rolled the home paddock for a car park. The local police had been informed and the AA had erected signs and directions. Microphones were installed, caterers had been engaged for the teas, and a table and chairs had been placed below the platform for the Press.

*   *   *   *

The farmers began to roll up from 1.30pm onwards and it wasn't long before they were poking about round the farm buildings. They were, of course, welcome to look around and I had Happy Tattersall show them round the large machinery shed. Happy was particularly pleased to show the visitors the two new Claas combine harvesters which had only been delivered five days before. Messrs. Ernest Doe and Sons, the machinery suppliers, had made certain that the combines were delivered in time for our big day.

Dudley Upshaw, my pig manager, in his best suit and collar and tie, conducted the visitors round the pig unit. The farrowing house, with its fifty farrowing pens, littered with fresh sawdust and wood shavings was a picture. Some pig farmers, when they enter a farrowing house, cannot resist counting the little pigs on each of the sows, and Dudley had seen that there were at least ten piglets on each sow. If a sow had a poor litter then Dudley would marry the piglets up with sows that had had over a dozen. The sixty carry on pens and the weaner pools, each holding a hundred growing pigs, and the sow yards were all littered with soft white barley straw. The animals were quiet and seemed happy in their environment. I should think that Dudley Upshaw was the best pig manager in England.

Helmet Hass, assisted by his wife, Linda, who had been trained in the NDP poultry course at Harper Adams, looked after the poultry unit as if it was their own.

Helmet was one of my very best workers. He had been a prisoner of war and had married Linda Clitheroe, a land girl from Wickham Market. They had three children and lived in one of our cottages. Helmet, who had been an unter officer, had driven a German Mark III tank in the 21st Panzer Division, in the North African Desert War. He had been captured at Sidi Rezegh during the British breakout from the Tobruk Siege, in November 1941. Helmet and I had decided that we had been within a mile of each other on 25th November 1941 when the Tobruk Garrison had pressed home its attack southwards towards the El Adam aerodrome and Sidi Rezegh. Helmet, in fact, had been captured by the Second New Zealander Division on the high ground where, with our twenty five pounders, we had pulversided the German 21st Division on the exposed pitch ridge of El Duda.

The pelvic bones in the two thousand pullets in the pullet rearing houses were widening and their combs were reddening towards the point of lay. Helmet had entered two pens of pullets for the National Laying Trials, and by handling the birds daily and feeling the spreading pin bones he could select two pens of birds and almost guarantee that the birds would be laying within forty eight hours of arriving at the testing station.

It was a hatching day and there was always a tingling, warm thrill and a hurry of the spirit when, on the twenty first day, the great incubator doors were opened and the vast trays were filled with thousands of hatching, cheeping chicks, many of them not yet dry.

Amongst the farmers, who were watching the hatching and the packing of the chicks, were several of our customers and so we were glad to show them round.

All my managers had good, well-paid jobs with me, and they all lived in comfortable cottages with modern kitchens and central heating. They had excellent salaries and were paid no overtime but all of them would work right through a weekend and into the late hours of the night if necessary.

*   *   *   *

Sir Henry Plumb arrived at around two o'clock, in Gordon Shottsford's Land Rover, and with him were Jim Patterson and Randal Gibbs, our two County NFU delegates to Headquarters. The general impression of Sir Henry amongst the farmers was that he was a 'farmers' man'. He had successfully argued the case for farmers at the Annual Price Reviews, his feet were firmly on the ground, and he was a worthy President of the National Farmers' Union.

I had met Sir Henry on a few occasions when, as Chairman of our County Arable and Livestock Committee, I had gone up to the NFU Headquarters at Knightsbridge for special meetings.

When Sir henry alighted from the Land Rover he came over to me and shook hands and said, "I understand, Albert, that you have a new automated fattening house for two thousand pigs, could I have a look at it?"

When I took Sir Henry over to the fattening house, Dudley had already switched on the power to the control panel. The panel was a confusion of pumps and switches and flashing lights, and was connected to each of the individual valves over the feeding troughs of the pens. "Now show me how you feed the pigs," said Sir Henry. Dudley just pressed the start button and predetermined amounts of feed and water were pumped through the three inch pipes into the troughs in the feeding pens. It was all over in ten minutes, and two thousand pigs had been fed and all the stockman had to do was to press a button. "That," said Sir Henry, "was very impressive."

*   *   *   *

Sir Henry walked into the corn store and climbed up the wooden step ladder onto the flat bottomed buck of the farm waggon. The farmers found seats on the bales of straw. Some of the farmers present had expanded their holdings during the War and they had borrowed money and had become prosperous. The majority of those present, however, were farming less than two hundred acres and they were spinning out with a relatively modest standard of living. The visit of Sir Henry was a great occasion and they had come from far and wide to listen to their President.

Sir Henry began by saying that many people said that East Anglia was the heartland of British agriculture. With its fertile and productive land and modern, efficient farmers it was providing much of the food consumed by the British people and its grain was the basis of much of our meat and milk production.

"Our farmland," went on Sir Henry, "is a national asset to be prized above a few decades of North Sea Oil. Our farmers and growers, supported by their workers, scientists and technicians, have succeeded in increasing the proportion of Britain's fifty six million people that can be fed from our own domestic resources."

Speaking without notes, Sir Henry went on, "East Anglian farmers have responded magnificently to the challenge and have played a leading role in this achievement. They can and will, given the resources, continue to do so. All they seek is a fair deal for their industry." This remark brought many cries of "hear, hear", and a volume of clapping from the farmers.

Sir Henry took a sip of water, and he then went on to talk about the European Economic Community and the Common Agricultural Policy.

"It seems that today the French, with their very small holdings, are concerned for the peasants but the British Government is concerned for the housewives, although, of course, both are really concerned with votes." This comment brought smiles and nods to the faces of the audience. "Public opinion throughout Europe will not go on tolerating lakes of wine or mountains of butter which owe their existence to a policy of justice for the small farmer. "One thing that the Government and Opposition appear to agree on is the need to maintain a cheap food policy. It is now beginning to look as though the NFU has got its work cut out to defend the CAP from the political expediency of both major parties. They appear to be becoming increasingly more concerned with a Cheap Agricultural Policy than a Common one!"

Sir Henry spoke for nearly an hour and sat down to much applause.

*   *   *   *

It had been a good day for Julie and me, and I had received many compliments, particularly with regard to our pig and poultry units.

Ben Purchase, a three thousand acre Lincolnshire farmer, offered to give me two thousand pounds to take his son, Colin, as a student for a year. Chris Holmes, of the *Farmers Weekly*, asked if he could fix a day when he could come over and give the farm a write up. Dr. Philip Barber, the Vice-Principal of the East Anglian Agricultural College, fixed up two evenings when he could bring the National Diploma students round.

Julie was putting away the coffee cups and she said, "Now don't get big-headed, there are plenty of farmers round here as good as you."

"Yes," I said, full of cunning, "but they haven't got such a beautiful wife as I have."

"Toad eating, soft soap and apple sauce," said Julie, coming over and giving me a little kiss, "will get you everywhere."

CHAPTER TWENTY-THREE

Saturday Night

It was Saturday night in the 'Dog and Duck'. Happy Tattersall, Alf Potts and Bert Hick were getting through their Saturday night session. They were tired of dominoes and were now on the third game of darts with 701 up. They were taking a long time finishing off the game and were having great difficulty in getting a 'double one'. They were all full of beer.

"The darts ent na bloody good," grumbled Happy, as his dart struck the wall a good nine inches off the board. "They want some new fevvers."

Big bosomed Rosie Briggs, behind the bar, overheard Happy and said, "You don't want to blame the darts, Happy. They were new last month. I don't reckon you hold the dart proper and the trouble is you're ganty gutted and runnin' to pod. That last dart you threw missed the board by two feet. You'd do better with yer head in a sack."

Alf and Bert had a bit of a laugh when Rosie was frisky, and Happy, who would like to have stuck a live rabbit down Rosie's jumper, was incapable of composing an appropriate response. He said, "Don't let's have none of your sauce, Rosie. Oi allus howd the dart proper and Oi keeps me arm plumpendickerler."

"Plumpendickerler?" enquired Bert.

"Yes," said Happy. "You can't hardly goo wrong wiv a dart if yer howd yer arm plumpendickerler."

The taproom door opened and Walt and Stumpy chuddled in. Stumpy had spent most of the afternoon nailing toe and heel tips on his hobnails. "Evenin' all," said Walt.

Bert Hick said, "Watcha, Walt, me owd sparrer. Where yer bin lately?"

"About and about," said Walt, "got a sooty chimbly. Had ter git the brush from Sid. Heard the latest?"

"What's that," said Alf Potts, as he flicked his lighter and drew on his Woodbine.

"Just saw the Vicar come owt the orf licence," said Walt, "with a coupla bottles. Wouldja believe it?"

"That be buggered for a tale," said Alf, "dunt come any of that lumber. Yew goo and look daft somewhere else."

"True as Oi stand 'ere," said Walt, "an' Oi'll tell yer what, he were lookin' somethin' shifty an all. He were twitchin' loike an owd moorhin's tail."

"When were that, then?" said Alf.

"S'arternoon," said Walt, "arter dinner."

"Well, Oid never hev thought it," said Alf, "thought he only drank holy water and the communion wine what's left over."

"Haps he was a'lookin' in the orf licence to see if Nobby Stripe were in there so he could tell him orf," said Stumpy.

This remark amused Walt, who was the life and soul of the taproom, no end and he was overcome by a wave of mirth. As Bert said afterwards, "Walt laughed fit ter bust hisself. He was lollopin' about and he laughed loike he'd never leave orf an' bloody nearly fell orf his bar stool."

In fact, Walt laughed so much that he took a swipe at Stumpy. Stumpy, however, was ready for him and did a sharp sidestep to the left and Walt caught his hand on the edge of the door. "Yew silly owd bugger," said Walt, holding his painful hand, "what d'yer hev ta dew that for?"

"Oi've had enough of yew hittin' me when yew larf, Oi'm proper drove up, yew bloody well hit somebody else."

Bert Hick changed the subject. "Bin some muddlesome owd weather," he said, "B'aint done the taters no good. Taters is wunnerful poor this year, little owd twindley bines and Oi can't see the clog wheat comin' ta more'n ten coombe."

"None the more for that," said Alf. "There's a good owd hang of apples and Oi've got everlastin' marrers this year. Oi'm buggered if Oi don't knock moi apples orf afore the owd waspies git 'em. T'other year they played hemp along a'moi owd apples and plums. They owd waspies is a unbominable pest."

"Talkin' of Nobby," said Bert, "heard how Nobby is?"

Nobby had fallen over and chinked his back. "He was all shook up. He's still ill abed. Reckon he wunt be back at wuk till Monday come fortnight."

"Dunt wonder at it, larsh Wensdy he were drunk as a fiddler's bitch, he bibble loike a duck. His owd woman got onto him an' all, talk about ban and blast. She do take on. She clickit loike an owd magpie."

"She ban and blast all the toime. Oi never could git along a'she. She's an opputary owd puss an' gits proper bewoggled."

"She do an' all," said Bert, who had more than once been on the wrong edge of Mrs. Stripe's tongue.

"Oi see she yisty," said Alf, "goon ter the tater field."

"On her owd boike?"

"No. Course not, Shank's pony. She weren't half boxin' along. She's a case she is. She walk straight as an owd boar thistle."

"Nobby dunt git up very for'ard in the mornin' an' when he do git up, half the toime he jist podge and wamble about. So she has to goo dollopin' along tidy fast ter git the wuk done. Oi know fer a fact, one mornin' she gutted twenty rabbits afore breakfast."

"They say," said Bert, "that Nobby's eldest granddaughter is goon ter git married."

Alf said, "Dunt know what she want ter git married fer sa quick, she aint big yet. She baffle me proper – bangled it up and made a roight bloody mess on it."

"Well," said Happy, "she arsed fer it, clanjanderin' about with they two owd booys from Middlesham, that goo abowt in that ramshackle owd moty car. It was that owd booy what she met when he pinched her bum, firework noight, so they say. Oi see she with one o' the owd booys in the High Field ditch jist afore harvest. They was hevin a goo in the Barn Field wheat."

"Cor," said Bert. "If they'd bin hevin a goo in Barn Field a week later, when we was harvestin', they'd both have gorn straight fru the concubine."

"Concubine?" said Happy.

"Stands ter reason," said Bert.

CHAPTER TWENTY-FOUR
At The Royal

It was two years later, during the late morning of the first day of The Royal Show, at Stoneleigh, that I ran into Wilfred Barraclough. He had been looking at alternative software for his computer in the High Tec stand. It was a hot day, and when Wilfred asked me to go and have a drink with him in the Members' Club I was only too pleased to join him.

Wilfred was in many ways old-fashioned but, particularly on money matters, he was very shrewd. It was put about that Wilfed had made two major killings on the Stock Exchange. Two years earlier he had strongly advised me not to plough all our profits back into the farm, but to spread it around in other ways. He had, in fact, strongly recommended me to buy gold shares. I had done what Wilfred had advised and two years later the price of gold had shot up by four times the purchase price, and I had instructed my broker to sell the lot. I now had two hundred thousand pounds to invest.

"I reckon," said Wilfred, "that those gold shares I told you to buy have paid better than your old pigs."

"You're right, Wilfred," I said, "and a damned sight less work."

"What do you reckon you'll do with your windfall?" said Wilfred.

"I don't know what to do," I said, "the bank interest hardly keeps up with inflation and the building societies aren't much better."

"You'd be as well to keep half of your money in one of the building societies' high interest accounts and some of the National Savings options are worth considering but, whatever you do, don't gamble with the lot."

"I won't do that," I said, "but I enjoy a bit of a flutter, and I don't get turned on by ICI and Courtaulds and the blue chips and I bought a couple of combines two years ago so I am not looking for large sums in machinery depreciation."

Coming through the entrance to the Members' Club, carrying his shooting stick and wearing a large Panama hat, was Richard Salter. I had given Richard first prize when I had judged the East of England Farm competition, two years previously. Richard farmed three thousand acres in Cambridgeshire, and he was one of the best and most successful farmers in the County. He was well set up and he had two horses in training and flew his own aeroplane. He was big in tomatoes and had thirty six acres of glass. He had made a lot of money growing celery, asparagus, daffodil bulbs and blackcurrants. He was master of his job. He recognised me and came over. "Hullo, Albert," he said, ordering a gin and tonic from the waitress, "I haven't seen you since you came round farm judging."

"No," I said, "but I keep an eye on you through the Farming Press. How did you get on in the Farm Competition this year?"

"They only gave me second," he said, "we had the grandfather of a thunderstorm a week before the judges came round, and it flattened two hundred acres of Winter Wheat. It looked as if we had taken the rolls over it."

"Too much nitrogen?" I asked.

"Not really," said Richard, "I only gave it eighty units."

I introduced Wilfred and said, "This is Wilfred Barraclough, one of my near neighbours and he is my tame financial adviser."

"Albert doesn't want a lot of advising," said Wilfred, "he can look after himself all right. Come and join us."

Richard put his drink on the table, pulled out a chair, hung his shooting stick on the back and sat down.

"We were just discussing," went on Wilfred, "that if we had a considerable amount of money to invest, what would we do with it, providing we weren't in a hurry to get our money back."

"I have no hesitation in telling you what to do," said Richard.

"What's that?" I said.

"I should put the lot into Lloyds."

"What, Lloyds of London?"

"Yes. You can't go wrong. I've been a Name for over ten years and for the last eight years I have never had less than fifteen thousand pounds a year, and there is a nice little loophole where you can save by putting your money into reserves."

"Sounds like a licence to print money," I said, "what do I have to do to join?"

"Well," said Richard, "you have to become a Name at Lloyds and once you have joined you effectively become a trader in the risk business and in the commercial insurance and reinsurance, in which Lloyds specialises. To join Lloyds you have to show that you have net assets of a hundred thousand pounds and this amount will be sure to be raised in the years to come."

"Would the value of your house be included in that?" I asked.

"Not your principal residence," said Richard, "but it would include quoted shares that you own at market value, cash, the surrender value of life insurance policies and some other forms of wealth."

"What would be my first move, then?" I said.

"Well," said Richard, "the initial contact with the Lloyds authorities is made through one of the one hundred and ninety members' agents and, assuming he was satisfied with your credentials, he would sponsor you as a Name for membership of Lloyds. He would then advise you on which of the three hundred and fifty four syndicates to join."

"It seems to me that you would be placing a lot of faith in your agent's judgement."

"That's true," said Richard, "I will introduce you to my man if you wish."

"What other advantages are there over investing in equities?" I said.

"A major advantage is that one third of your premium, up to seven thousand pounds, can be invested in a special reserve and this sum is deductable against income tax."

"That's useful," I said. "How are the syndicates managed?"

"The syndicates are managed by another class of agency group, and these managing agents are responsible for appointing a professional underwriter and his support staff."

"It seems to me," I said, "that once you've paid your premiums you have little or no control of your money."

"That's right," said Richard, "and what is more, if your syndicate makes an overall loss you are individually liable for your share of the loss. I can only say that over the years, I have had some very pleasing results and profits."

*   *   *   *

That evening, driving back to the hotel with Julie I said, "I think I know what to do with the money from our gold shares."

"What's that?" said Julie.

"Put it into Lloyds," I said.

"Have you thought it through?" said Julie.

"Yes," I said, "Richard Salter gets an income most years of some fifteen thousand pounds from the profits from his syndicates."

"You do realise," said Julie, "that if you get into the wrong syndicates and someone blows up three Jumbo jets, or a passenger liner sinks with all passengers, or two or three hurricanes decide to run riot, that you stand the risk of them taking the shirt off your back? Most of the Names haven't got a clue as to what's going on."

"How is it that you have suddenly become an expert in financial matters which are well beyond your comprehension?" I said.

"A male chauvinist pig like you might well ask," said Julie. "As a matter of fact, I have discussed these things with Major Carrington and Lady Helena. The Major is in his wheelchair nearly all day and he rings up his broker every morning. I had a chat with the Major about Lloyds a fortnight ago, and he said that the average return for a Name underwriting two hundred thousand pounds isn't worth the risk of bankruptcy. It seems to me," went on Julie, "that when people have wealth they spend half their time worrying up schemes to save tax. I'm afraid that I am a simple girl and I don't see why those of us that are well off shouldn't pay our proper taxes. And don't run away with the idea that Lloyds is a generous welfare agency. What you had better do, Albert, is to put half of the money into high interest accounts and the other half into equities, and then you can enjoy yourself studying the share prices in the *Financial Times* every morning."

As I switched off the engine after parking the car in the hotel car park in Stratford, I said, "I can see that you are in one of your bossy moods Julie, but perhaps we won't put our money into Lloyds after all."

That night, at dinner, I ordered a bottle of champagne to celebrate our investment decision.

"You know," said Julie, "we farmers gamble quite enough already with Swine Fever, and Foot and Mouth, and Fowl Pest, and hailstorms just before harvest, and what is more," said Julie, smiling, "Mum said I took on quite a gamble when I married you."

She was leaning towards me across the table, the light catching her long eyelashes. I gave her a gentle kick under the table. "Marriage is a very risky business," I said, "but I'd rather have you than Lady Helena or the Bank Manager's wife."

"What about Gina Lolobrigida?" said Julie.

"That's different," I said, "have another glass of bubbly."

CHAPTER TWENTY-FIVE
Master Johnson

We had been farming and working hard for many years and we had taken on another three hundred and forty acres to rent when Julie said to me, "Albert, why don't you buy yourself a horse and then you can come out hunting with me. There are some good horses in the West Suffolk Hunt and there are some pretty girls for you to look at as well. Not only that, as you are a farmer you would get your hunting for nothing. There would be no subscription or cap to pay as you allow the Hunt to gallop all over your land. Quite seriously, the Hunt Committee are very pleased to see farmers and landowners with a horse."

"They know which side their bread is buttered and fifty horses galloping across my farm can do more damage than the cost of three years' subscriptions. Anyway," I went on, "I hear you killed a yellow cat last season."

"We don't talk about that," said Julie.

"You were very lucky," I said "that the Hunt Secretary was on good terms with the Editor of the *Gazette*, otherwise you would have had the front page. Sometimes I feel like joining the 'antis' from the University that come out blowing bugles and laying false trails, anyway it costs about twenty quid for a set of shoes."

"Don't be mean," said Julie, "you don't shoot and you don't play golf and you want something to take your mind off your old farm now and again. All work and no play makes Jack a dull boy."

"Yes," I said, "and it makes Jill into a well to do widow."

"However," Julie persisted, "there is no better way of seeing all your crops than from the back of a horse, and another attraction of having a horse on a farm is that the cost of the horse, its keep and its stabling can be lost in the farm accounts." Julie had it all worked out.

*   *   *   *

To tell you the truth, if I didn't hunt I would be against hunting because everything you read about hunting makes it sound indefensible.

I would tease Julie. "Poor old fox," I would say, "chased by wild people on horses that run away with you and then torn to pieces by a pack of rapacious hounds."

"There is another side to it," said Julie. "Foxes have to be controlled so that they don't kill large numbers of chickens and lambs, and you may not know that a vixen and her cubs will, in one square mile, kill fifty pheasants, ducks and partridges in a season. Up North, farmers will pay ten pounds for a fox shot at lambing time."

"Then why not shoot them?" I said.

"Well," said Julie, "unless you are very close to a fox you will not kill it with a twelve bore and the chances are that the fox will be wounded and gangrene will set in and that could be a very painful and lingering death. The same thing applies to poison or gassing or catching them in a snare, they can be a long time dying, and even you weren't too happy when last year a fox got into one of your special breeding pens of Light Sussex and you found thirty hens with their heads bitten off."

"I don't mind a fox taking the odd hen to eat," I said, "but when they get into a pen of poultry they go berserk and will kill for the hell of it."

"I think that you had better come out hunting with us," said Julie, "and you will soon see that we don't kill many foxes. As a matter of fact I have a certain respect for the genuine animal lovers who are against hunting if they also try and stop people fishing. You can't tell me that the poor old salmon enjoys being played with for up to three quarters of an hour with a hook through its mouth."

"They'll never stop fishing," I said.

"Why not?" said Julie.

"Because," I said, "a million people fish in the U.K. and any government that tried to stop fishing would be out at the next election. The 'antis' only attack minority sports. Marcus Hurd, our M.P. was telling me at the Show that he was against blood sports, but I noticed that he was tucking into his salmon sandwiches. And another thing," I said, "I hear all sorts of scandalous goings on among some of your hunting friends. Peter told me that Pongo Forbes-Atkinson, your Hunt Secretary, is rather keen on Sir Alfred Dawson's wife."

"Oh," said Julie, "that's been going on for a long time but I understand that Sir Alfred went along one night to have it out with Pongo, and there was a bit of a skirmish and Sir Alfred hit Pongo on the head with a shovel. The next day was a Saturday and Pongo came out hunting looking like a battered panda."

"I hope that Nigel Dempster doesn't get hold of that," I said.

*   *   *   *

Eight days later Julie and I set off to look at a horse that was advertised in the *Horse and Hound*. We took Peter and Sally along with us although neither of them knew the first thing about a horse. In fact, Sally always said that her Uncle Robert had told her that the main thing to know about a horse is to 'beware both ends and avoid the middle'.

The horse was described as a bay gelding, sixteen hands, sound and traffic proof and a good hunter. He had been hunted with the Cambridgeshire Harriers. Then, in brackets, the advertisement read 'not a novice ride'.

"Look at that," I said, "I expect that he will pull your arms out of their sockets, and that he has got a mouth like a bag of spanners. I could do with a steady old cob."

"Anyone would think that you're an old man," said Julie, "I happen to know that this horse takes a bit of a hold, but he is quiet and good tempered and has no vice. I've been talking to Joe Pickersgill, the huntsman, and he says that he knows the horse and the only reason the Robinsons are parting with it is that he is a bit too much of a handful for Mrs. Robinson and their fifteen year old boy. Joe thinks that you ought to buy it."

*   *   *   *

There was no doubt that this bay horse that we had come down to see at Cherry Hinton really looked the part. He was compactly made and had plenty of bone. He had a nicely moulded, intelligent head, with a kind eye, full of courage and honesty. He had well-shaped sloping shoulders, a short back and powerful quarters. His legs were as clean as a whistle. The Robinson's groom, who had been a Head Lad at Newmarket, led the horse into a thirty acre field which had been put down to grass for the Robinson's two hundred cow herd of British Friesians.

"What's his name?" enquired Julie.

"We call him Master Johnson," said the groom, "he's by the same stallion that sired Kilmore that won the Grand National, with Fred Winter up."

"Well, we're not looking for a Grand National winner at the moment, but we should like to get hold of a horse that could run into a place in an open point to point," I said.

"This horse takes a bit of a hold but he has got a fair turn of speed and he will stay for ever," said the groom."

*   *   *   *

The groom gave me a leg up and I swung my leg over the saddle and took Master Johnson into the flat grass ley. I trotted him once round the field, and then took him twice round at a sharp canter and put him over a low post and rails and a brush fence that was used for schooling the youngsters, and, although he took hold of the bit, I had no trouble pulling him up.

When I brought Master Johnson back to the gate, Sally said, "I think you should buy him, Albert."

"And what makes you think I should buy him?" I said.

"Well," said Sally, "he's got a lovely face and a very long tail, with two grey hairs in it, and pretty ears."

"Sally," I said, "I wouldn't trust you to go out and buy me a donkey."

Julie, looking the part, had come down in her oatmeal jumper, jodhpurs, tied a scarf round her head and said, "I'd like to give him a pipe opener along the far side headland. He looks as if he might make a point to pointer."

I gave her a leg up and shortened the leathers and handed her my whip. Julie pushed Master Johnson into a brisk canter down to the far end of the pasture. She then turned him into the headland by the hedge and then kicked the big bay into a gallop. The horse knew what was expected of him and, without whip or spur, he swept into a fierce gallop and cut away at a cracking pace. He was covering the ground like a true stayer.

When Julie brought him in, Master Johnson's flanks were hardly moving. "He's three parts fit already," said Julie, who seemed to know about these things.

"They're asking two thousand for him," I said, "I expect that we'd better have him subject to our own vet giving him the all clear."

"Yes," said Julie, "I think that we have a rather exceptional horse here."

"How much should we give the groom?" I said.

"If you were in a restaurant," said Julie, "you would have to give him two hundred pounds, but I think that he should be very happy to have a couple of tenners."

So that is what we did and three days later Bill Fox, renowned for cattle haulage and a regular attender at all the shows, sales and markets, was off in his very swish, four compartment horse box to collect Master Johnson.   He arrived back with our bay gelding about lunch time and Master Johnson was quietly led down the side running board and into his new home. We put him into our best loose box looking out over the yard where he could talk to the cattle and see what was going on.

CHAPTER TWENTY-SIX
The Hunt

It was a fresh, cold, bright January morning when Julie and I set out for a Saturday Lawn Meet which was to be held at Great Langham Hall, the magnificent home of Sir Alistair and Lady Ponsford.

There was still a touch of frost and the woods and hedges were a crystal kingdom – a sparkling world of motionless glass. Happy Tattersall said that it was "Farmers' weather, because you had to work hard to keep warm."

Julie was on Silver Rain, looking as neat as a wheatsheaf, and I was on Master Johnson, who was high-spirited and full of corn and who had not been out of his box for two days, and was feeling his toes. He was tossing his fine head, and wheeling sideways up against the railings as he edged along the road. He was excited and no doubt looking forward to mixing in with the field.

"I shouldn't let him do that," said Julie, anxiously.

"Oh, shut up, Julie," I said, "I'm not *letting* him do it. How do you stop a great big animal that weighs over half a ton from going sideways if he wants to?"

"You'll have to see that Happy cuts down on his oats," said Julie, faintly amused at my fiery steed.

A mile or so away from Great Langham Hall we were joined by Fred Packer, a retired cosmetics manufacturer. Fred, red-faced, and already lubricated by dry Martinis, had a fat cigar in his mouth. He weighed sixteen stone, had an insecure waistline, and rode like a sack of manure and, although tending to bulky corpulence, considered himself, according to Julie, to be a muscular poem in the saddle. Fred, a slum boy from the East End, was a self-made man and was always bulling on about his early hardships. He was disgustingly wealthy and wallowed in affluence and he reckoned, with some justification, that he had 'made it'. His car was a long-nosed, maroon Jag with a silver horse on the bonnet. His neo-Georgian house had four lavatories.

The trouble with Fred was that he had more than an eye for the women and he had a varied matrimonial track record. His first wife was an ex-stripper, and it had cost him a lot of money when he got one of his girl grooms pregnant.

Fred had boasted that over 90% of his cosmetics were water or chalk, and he said that if you can sell the public plenty of chalk and water in small, pretty cunningly designed jars with thick bottoms you couldn't go wrong.

Fred was on a big-boned, weight carrying, chestnut that must have set him back a couple of thousand. He was a fully paid up member and he had made several generous contributions to the Hunt, and so he was fully entitled to be resplendent in his top hat and scarlet coat with hunt buttons and collar facings. It was strange to think that Fred, in spite of his gleaming spendour, had been seen eating eels and mash at the dogtrack at Walthamstow.

Fred raised his hat to Julie and I acknowledged. "Morning, Albert. Morning Julie."

"Morning, Fred," we said.

"Sharpish frost in the night," said Fred.

"Yes," I said, "it's not enough to get into the plough and it takes three consecutive hard frosts to stop hunting."

"Horse looks well, Albert," said Fred, eyeing Master Johnson as he pranced down the road, sideways.

"Yes," I said, "Julie reckons we shall have to cut down on his oat ration."

"If you should ever think of selling him, let me know." Fred had a good eye for a horse and with his deep pocket often got his way.

"We are unlikely to be parting with him," I said, "we think that he might make a good point to pointer."

I knew that Fred had a well-mannered little grey that his son, Tim, was hoping to race. However, the horse had cracked a cannon bone, and they were getting a little worried at the time it was taking to heal.

We were joined by others going to the Meet.

*   *   *   *

At the Meet hats were doffed right and left. There was a mixture of old shire landowners, working farmers and a sprinkling of the brash, newly rich, with their grooms and splendid boxes. It was a baffling social complexity with clipped county accents clashing affably with the rural burrs.

Ex-cattle dealer, seventy year old Herbert 'Baggy' Chambers was out, an ugly, good-natured man with long side-burns. He was on his shaggy cob and he raised his hat to wealthy landowner, Lord Wallace Tivendale and gave a cheery, "Good mornin', m'Lord. Grand huntin' mornin'."

The huntsmen and hounds were in the centre of the home paddock, below the ha-ha, at the base of Sir Alistair's six acre garden. The hounds were a moving carpet of black, white and tan. The butler and two maids, with rosy faces and snowy aprons, were moving round among the field carrying silver trays and offering warm sausage rolls and cherry brandy.

The Master, Major William Hawkins MFH, with grey hair and a military moustache, was now in his late sixties. Booted and spurred, he entered the arena on a huge black horse. There was a sense of feudal order. The Major's back was impossibly straight and his boots gleamed. His breeches and gloves were spotless white and his jacket blazed scarlet. He was well able to find the three thousand pounds a year which was his contribution to the cost of hunt servants, hounds and horses.

He was a great breeder of hounds and was a regular judge at the Annual Peterborough Hound Show. His name met with respectful nods in pink coated circles. He maintained good control of the field and was a stern critic of any member of the Hunt who rode his horse over a farmer's winter wheat. The Master was always reminding Hunt members that hunting was about good manners and fair play and respect for the fox and not just riding very quickly and jumping over fences.

He had done a lot of big game shooting when serving with the 21st Lancers, in India, and the preserved head of a tiger, which the Major had shot in Bengal in 1934, was nailed to the wall in the Trophy Room.

Jilly Bailey was out. Jilly was twenty two, a plain girl who was secretary to an estate agent in the City. Nearly every penny she earned and saved was spent on her horse, Measles, which was at livery. Measles was a red chestnut mare with four white legs and had seen the best of her days. Jilly had bought Measles out of a bakery cart for sixty pounds. Jilly was a charming girl, and many of the wealthier members of the Hunt would help out with her subscription or a loan of their horse box for a distant meet and she was thrilled when she was asked to go on the Ball Committee.

Riders, attired in scarlet and black, came in from all directions, and the roadside verges were crammed with cars, trailers and lorries. Ramps were lowered and horses clattered out on to the ground.

*   *   *   *

Audrey Hunter-Johnson was out. Audrey was a stunning, loose member of the frail sisterhood and a woman of pleasure and was always set up for sale. She was doe-eyed, long-legged with auburn hair and she foamed like root beer.

Audrey was mounted on a quiet grey which had been lent to her by Eton educated businessman, Algernon Boot. Audrey's father was a porter in the fish market in Billingsgate. Somehow he had organised a few unofficial, private fish deliveries and, together with his tips and bribes, and a cash job in the afternoons, he was earning more than any bank manager and paid considerably less in Income Tax. Mr. Abe Johnson, for that was his name, was in a financial position to suffer Audrey's indulgencies. Audrey took courses in elocution and modelling and she drove a very stylish, bright red MG sports car.

Audrey had syrupy eyes and an attractive seductive voice, and she had crowded a lot of experience into her short life. Indeed she had come a long way since operating from a high class call girl ring based on a certain well-known London hotel.

Audrey had found temporary comfort in the arms of Algy Boot but, although well-bred, Algy would be unable to keep Audrey in the style to which she had become accustomed from her London earnings. She, therefore, was only accepting the existing situation until something better turned up. She was really looking for an elderly multi-millionare with a title. It has to be admitted that although Audrey's chances of pulling this off were far from good, she would look well as hostess and doing the honours in some of the great houses of England. She was now intending to fish in the Quorn and Pytchley country where she had heard rumours of two brothers, aged eighteen and twenty one, who were sons of a millionare duke of the realm, who owned twenty thousand acres in Gloucestershire and Warwickshire and several streets in the Square Mile. Audrey had learned that the brothers were indolent, burned daylight and were eating the bread of idleness. They both hunted with the Quorn and had a reputation for wild parties with wild women. Audrey made plans to reconnoitre the state of play. She had long learned that time spent on reconnaissance was seldom wasted.

A photograph had appeared in one of the magazines on the very top shelf of the Middlesham Bookshop of Audrey wearing high-heeled leather boots and nothing else. It had been rumoured that she had attended the Hunt Ball, dressed to kill, in a dark green dress with a deep cleavage and although she was wearing suspenders and her stockings were drawn up to the limit, she was wearing no knickers.

Audrey had been very disappointed at Cowes last year where her target had left her after three days and had gone back to his wife.

*   *   *   *

Ollie Dibble, the twenty three year old 'ner do well' son of 'Tinker' Dibble, the owner of the local garage, was out. Ollie had mended a puncture on a motor bike and put a pint of sealant into Mrs. Tate's leaky radiator before he came to the Meet.

Ollie was riding a big, tough, unmanageable, ignorant sort of horse with a wall eye. The horse was shallow sided with a small, plain head and, according to Happy Tattersall, was so useless the the knacker's cart was too good for it. "That hoss," he said, "ain't wuth a worn out tail bandage," and he predicted that one day it would run into something solid and "break it's neck".

Tom Bannerman, the Huntsman, in scarlet coat, gleaming polished buttons, and boots burnished like mirrors, blew his horn and the Field moved off with the morning sun streaming out its thin warmth. The music of two hundred iron shoes on the hard, metalled road surface were echoing like a first year woodpecker in a smithy. A long trot brought us to the edge of Lords Wood, the property of Sir George Willoughby-Tench, a staunch preserver of foxes.

Tom Bannerman, who at 5.00am that morning had cut up a casualty ewe to feed hounds on their return from hunting, put the hounds in to draw the wood and the small willow plantation at the north end.

Soon a chorus of view-halloos proclaimed that a magnificent dog fox had sprung from the covert and was running swiftly for the open. Tom, who had recently joined the West Suffolk as huntsman from his previous place as second whip to the Pytchley, soon clapped the hounds on line.

The Master and Captain Piers Dawkins, a thruster if ever there was one, and on a clever chestnut mare, and Julie, who was never one to go round looking for a gate, were the first to jump over the roadside ditch onto the headland and away to the wide tree-lined ride which had been cleared for a fire break.

Julie had left me well behind and Master Johnson was tense, and restless like an overloaded spring. I turned him to the ditch and he sprung at it like a cat. He was surefooted and clever and was raring to go. We were soon galloping hard through the spongy turf of the ride. There was a slight splash of rain and the keen winter smell of the woods. It was a wild, uninhibited pleasure to ride this strong, mettlesome six year old, taking a keen hold, stretching his legs and eager to press forward and to keep pace with the leaders.

The hounds, which will sometimes cover five thousand miles in a season, were running like smoke and checked in the corner of Weald Wood and swinging uphill, they checked again near the farm buildings at Shatter Bushes. I joined a small group who were waiting for hounds to find the line. Here I caught up with Julie. Silver Rain's grey coat was already splattered with mud.

"Where have you been?" said Julie, impishly.

"I had to see you safely over the ditch before I followed," I said, "otherwise I would have been waiting here for you."

Diana Fawcett-Smith, a good looking woman in her forties and now on her favourite chestnut mare, was with us. Diana, who was now on her third husband, said, "Are you two arguing again?"

"Yes," said Julie, "I can't do anything with him and he's annoyed that I left him behind."

"Well, if you don't want him, I don't mind taking him off you." Diana looked good in black and would sit with great composure on a settee at Claridges.

"If Julie doesn't behave herself, I might take you up on that," I said.

"He's only half trained and half the time he thinks he's still in the desert," said Julie, mischievously.

The hounds were giving tongue and at that moment the fox burst out of the bottom of the wood and was heading towards Kettlebury Springs.

Kicking our heels into our restless steeds, we were off again. I was determined to be one of the 5% who rode straight to hounds and let the rest career round the lanes and through the gates. The adrenalin was burning in my blood.

We splashed through the ford, and the hounds, with heads up and sterns down, were now running like quicksilver. There was a stiffish post and rails ahead. Julie and I were galloping side by side. Both Silver Rain and Master Johnson flew it, and it was clear that Master Johnson knew when to put in a short one. Straight ahead there was a five bar gate and in no way was I going to put Master Johnson to it. I didn't want to come a cropper or earn a reputation as a 'timber smasher'. Julie, however, had different ideas and she and Silver Rain leaped the gate like Pat Smythe, at Wembley.

I have heard it said that there is only one sport that is more exhilerating than skiing, and that is to ride in the Grand National. I would lower my sights, and say that to be galloping at thirty five miles an hour at a fence, fifty four inches high, with thundering hooves behind is a good enough thrill for me.

Behind us Eddie Molesworth, the fourteen year old son of Clayton Molesworth, had fallen foul of the Master when his over-corned pony had collided with the Second Whip. Clayton Molesworth, who had recently been fined two thousand pounds for share pushing, had been determined that his son should have a pony which could win a few gymkhanas. As is often the case, Clayton and his wife were far more concerned that Eddie should win prizes with his pony than Eddie was himself. The Molesworths exemplified the conflux of the gin and jodphur establishment and subjected Eddie to every excess of parental snobbery. So Clayton bought a pony which had won gymkhanas in the Midlands. The name of the pony was 'Jazz King' and it proved to be something of a tearaway. As planned, he had won a couple of gymkhanas in the summer holidays. However, when Eddie, who always ate his sandwiches on the way to the Meet, took Jazz King out hunting the pony nearly always ran away with him and he got into considerable trouble from the Master and the Field.

The hounds flew forward and surged down the first grass field running at a rare bat. The dog fox had taken off. The problem was to keep sight of the hounds. Bearing left by King Harry's Grove we ran through a small plantation of Christmas trees. A fox shot out of the other side and the hounds were soon onto him. It was quite clear from the music of the hounds running that this was a fresh fox and, as is quite common, it had switched with the hunted one.

We had already ridden nearly three miles at a fast gallop. A certain amount of time was lost when the hounds made a curious loop and lost scent on the plough by the Army Training Ground. It was found that the fox had run up one furrow, and had come back down another to throw the hounds off scent. Near the top of the hill the hounds hovered a moment before swinging themselves round in a spectacular cast and recovered the line.

The hounds were again in full cry and Charley, who knew a thing or two, and, when hunted, would run through a field of sheep or cattle, or would roll on a muckheap to disguise his scent had made for the river and was a field to the good, where he was lost. Julie said, "It is doubtful if Charley has crossed the river because he knows that 'a wet fox is a pongy fox'."

"Pongy fox?" I said.

"Yes," said Julie, "a pongy fox."

It had been a brisk run with a four mile point and I was more convinced than ever that Master Johnson could run well in a point to point.

Julie and I stayed to the end and we had ridden every yard of the run. It was half past four in the grey twilight and although we had run two foxes to earth in the main earth at Beeches Hill Wood, none had been killed. It was getting dark and Julie and I hacked back the four miles to Newton Green.

Happy Tattersall was waiting at the stable door, and he took Master Johnson and gave him a rub down with straw before putting on his New Zealand rug. Happy then came across to the kitchen and took out the bran and linseed mash which had been slowly cooking on the Aga, all afternoon.

*   *   *   *

As I soaked in a hot bath my mind flooded back to the days in the Western Desert when Field Marshal Von Rommel, known as 'The Desert Fox' had hunted us and pursued us while we were out on our mobile desert patrols in Southern Libya. We were operating with a troop of four guns, sometimes hundreds of miles behind the enemy lines, hiding up at night and attacking the enemy and their supply lines at dawn. In its own way, with the excitement and exhileration of the chase, with fox hunters risking life and limb, it stirred memories of my war experiences in the wide open spaces.

I could not feel guilty that I had survived the war and that I had enjoyed a day in the hunting field where I had thrilled to the cry of the hounds, the smell of the woods and the changing pattern of the sunlight as it rippled along the backs of the hounds as they turned to the line.

There was peace in the land that evening as dead leaves swirled in the January bluster and the chimneys were making ladders of smoke. Occasionally, a gust of wind would come along and sweep the clouds to the high west.

I had settled myself, with a book, in my armchair. Julie came downstairs in her dressing gown and her hair was hanging loose. It had been a wonderful day in the wild depths of the countryside, and we had had a wonderful year with farming at its zenith.

I was caught with the thought of what would have happened to us if we had lost the War. What would have happened if, after over-running Europe, Germany had attacked and invaded Britain instead of turning on Russia and what would have been the outcome if the Japanese had not bombed Pearl Harbor and brought the Americans into the War? What would have been the course of the War if we had not stopped and then defeated Rommel at Alamein? We had fought and won the inestimable treasure of liberty and now our haven seemed almost too secure.

Julie and I had our supper by the fire. How could we measure these golden growing years in the widening field of experience? They were mysteries and rewards in suspended time. It was a period of unrestrained happiness, and Julie and I laughed at the same things and we loved for every kind of reason. Julie was slim and warm, and I was feeding into fantasy as the night took the ultimate possession of the earth.

CHAPTER TWENTY-SEVEN
The House of Cards

Julie and I had been asked on two or three occasions whether we played Bridge. It so happened that when I was stationed at Helwan in the Nile Valley, just before Alamein, I had played quite a lot of Bridge when on leave in Cairo. My partners at the Bridge Club were Bob Fielding and Stephen Hooper, both of whom were first secretaries in the British Embassy. Our fourth member had been Hussein Abbas, an English-speaking Egyptian Civil Servant, who was something of a liaison officer between our High Commission and the Palace.

Peter Henderson had played Bridge both at school and also when he was at the Royal Agricultural College at Cirencester.

However, Julie and Sally had never played and they were very pleased to accept the invitation of Queenie Ames and Abigail Foskett to go along with them to the Bridge classes at the local Community Centre. They had all enrolled in the Beginners' Class.

The four 'girls' became quite keen and they looked forward to their Bridge and gossip on alternate Tuesday evenings. There was no doubt about it that Queenie and Abigail would never be candidates for the Bridge Master Class, as they tended to chatter and bubble away when hands were being played and they subscribed to as little mental inconvenience as possible.

The Ames and the Fosketts were older than us, but together with Peter and Sally, we had met up on a coach trip when the Middlesham Rotary Club had visited Hever Castle. We had all got on well together and we found the Fosketts and the Ames great fun. However, if you could hear them playing Bridge together you could be forgiven for being led to believe that divorces were imminent.

Queenie's husband, Jim, worked at Coutts Bank and he played Bridge at his London Club. Stuart Foskett was an area insurance manager and spent much time travelling round his district. He was considering taking early retirement.

Julie and I decided to arrange two tables of Bridge one evening and we had invited the Ames, the Fosketts, Peter and Sally over to Broadshots. The evening would be split up into two parts, with coffee, sandwiches and a large cake at half past eight marking a lengthy and gossipy half time.

Jim and Stuart were useful card players. They got their trumps out early and seldom overcalled. They preferred to play Bridge using recognised rules, conventions and systems, as laid down and recommended by Culbertson, Terence Rees and others. But, as I have said, Abigail and Queenie preferred chatty Bridge and tended to use the card table as a prop for the wider dispersal of news and scandal.

On this particular evening, Stuart and Abigail had had a furious row in the car driving over and it was with difficulty that they were able to maintain any semblance of sweetness and light on their arrival. They really had a happy marriage but they rowed constantly and threatened to leave each other about twice a week. However, an affectionate kiss from Jim and a large gin and tonic had a calming influence on Abigail's emotional botheration and discomposure.

* * * *

We drew cards and the Fosketts and the Ames were drawn on one table and Peter and Sally drew with us.

On one table, Jim spread out the pack and they drew cards to deal. Queenie drew the King of Spades and said that she would have the red pack with the horses and chinamen, and would sit on the chair with her back to the fire. Abigail, who was on Queenie's right, picked up the red cards and began to shuffle the pack.

"Shuffle in front and cut behind," said Stuart, sharply, snatching the pack from Abigail. Stuart shuffled the pack with a flourish, making much of the operation.

Queenie dealt the pack as if the cards had been dipped in marmalade and ended up one short. "Fourteen," said Jim, letting Queenie take her pick.

They picked up their cards.

Jim and Queenie had recently become grandparents. "How's the baby?" enquired Abigail.

"When the cards are up, shut up," said Stuart.

"Teething," said Queenie.

"I bet they'll hold the front page for that," said Jim.

"I was on the 'phone to Fiona, yesterday," went on Queenie, "and she had been up half the night. Spencer is no help. She should never have married him."

"You'd think there'd never been another grandmother," said Jim.

"She's too good for him," said Queenie. "Who dealt?"

"You did," said Jim, patiently.

"Did I?" said Queenie, somewhat surprised and sending out little vibrations of disdain.

Queenie examined her cards and counted up her points. "Did you get that green dress in Rankins?" she said.

"No. They'd only got size fourteen," replied Abigail.

"Get on with it," said Jim, making a grimace of sour exasperation.

"One Club," said Queenie.

"Phoney?" enquired Stuart.

"Yes," said Queenie.

"The good players don't play the phoney Club," said Stuart, frowning. "One heart."

"Two Clubs," said Jim.

"Pass," said Abigail.

"What's the calling been?" said Queenie.

"One Club, one Heart, two Clubs and Abigail had passed," said Jim.

"I don't know what I'll do," said Queenie, as she meditated her next step and slowly reviewed her options. "I think I'll go three Clubs. No, I won't. I'll pass."

"Oh, Gawd," said Jim. "Make up your mind."

So they played in two Clubs and when Queenie won the first trick and led the King of Hearts, Jim nearly went up the wall.

"What have I done now?" said Queenie, seeing Jim's look of astonishment.

"You'll see," said Jim, as they lost the next four tricks, "and hold your cards up, everyone can see them."

"Sorry," said Queenie.

"You wouldn't be allowed to chatter like that at the Club," said Jim, noticing Queenie's eyebrows arch slightly in these moments of confrontation.

"I wouldn't play Bridge at your bloody club, for all the tea in China," said Queenie, tartly. She got her two Clubs all right, and said, "I don't know what you were worried about, Jim."

"You never lead into your opponents' call," said Jim.

"We got our two Clubs, so you might as well shut up," said Queenie, mortified at what she considered her husband's dull supidity.

"Do you know," said Jim, seeking revenge, "yesterday, Queenie took an hour and a half upstairs to change her frock."

"That's nothing," said Queenie, "I've been waiting for Jim to put two screws in the kitchen door for five months."

Jim, looking slightly shamefaced, sipped his gin and tonic.

Stuart thought it advisable to change the subject. "Did you watch the Bridge on TV last night?" he said.

"I couldn't understand the calling," said Jim.

"Oh, I could," said Queenie, brightly.

"Of course," said Jim, deridingly, "Queenie reckons she's the Ricky Marcus of Middlesham. We all undervalue Queenie's expertise and her great contribution to the world of Bridge."

"I did all right that time, anyway," said Queenie, giving a little wink in our direction.

CHAPTER TWENTY-EIGHT
Visit to Fred Sayers

Julie had ridden in several point to points in the south east and had won two ladies' races the previous year on Lady Helena's horse, Thornbush. Thornbush was a big liver chestnut that had been brought over from Ireland as a four year old.

Julie had been determined to ride our own horse, Master Johnson, at the Cottenham Point to Point in the coming season.

It is letting out no secrets to say that we had taken Master Johnson down to Fred Sayers at his training establishment at Wimborne. I had met Fred when he was in charge of the Cavalry Division Remount Depot at Haifa in Palestine in 1940, and we had kept in touch ever since. Fred was one of the most successful trainers over the sticks in the south of England and he suggested that we should try out Master Johnson against a good form horse that he had in his stable called 'Maid in the Mist'. Maid in the Mist had run in handicap chases at Taunton and Market Raison and had been second on both occasions to two top class chasers both of which had gone on to win races worth over two thousand pounds.

*   *   *   *

It was a windy Wednesday morning when we took Master Johnson down to Fred in our horsebox.

Fred's daughter, Maxine, who rode out every morning with the string, was there to ride Maid in the Mist while Julie rode Master Johnson.

Fred had built seven fences round the headland of a ninety five acre field. Maxine and Julie would have to race round the course two and a half times for the three miles. Fred had planned the course so that there was a long uphill finish and many people in the racing world considered that one of the reasons that Fred was so successful and that he was able to get his horses fit and wound up before a race was that the uphill finish built up muscles and found out the weaknesses as well as the staying power of his horses.

*   *   *   *

Master Johnson was sweating and restless as I gave Julie a leg up. Maid in the Mist was looking well and at the peak of fitness. Maxine and Julie cantered over to the far side of the field to the start.

Fred, who was chewing a stem of fescue, and I had our field glasses trained on the two girls as they set off at a steady gallop along the north side of the course where Fred had his all weather track and soon two specs swung into view. They were now doing a fastish gallop and turned down by the spinney onto the quarter mile of straight. It was clear that Maid in the Mist was being hustled, and she was cutting her fences. Master Johnson, on the other hand, was giving his jumps plenty of daylight. The two horses came up to us with thudding hooves, galloping side by side as they flew the fence by the stack of bales.

There was nothing between them as they came round and swept past us for a second time and Fred looked at his watch. "Two seconds faster then I thought," said Fred, almost to himself.

Back on the home stretch it was clear that Master Johnson was going the better of the two, and Maxine clipped the top of the second last and made the fir fly. A furlong from home the two girls asked their mounts for a storming finish. Although Maid in the Mist was a game mare, she was being destroyed as Master Johnson began to pull away and he was a good two lengths clear at the post.

"You've got a good sort there," said Fred, putting away his watch, "I wouldn't mind having him in my yard. He should be able to set things alight and win two or three opens for you next season."

CHAPTER TWENTY-NINE
The Races

It was the day of the West Suffolk Point to Point and, after the dry winter, there had been enough rain to soften the top two inches of turf on the race course and to make the going good.

It was a mild April day and the countryside was wide awake with mating and nesting and procreation. The morning sun was lighting flames like red sores licking the bowl of the beech trees. The water, smooth in the pond, was like blue glass under the sunlight. Young rooks were flexing their wings. The apple and plum trees in our orchard were dressed in blossom and the ditches were full of primroses.

We had planned to give Master Johnson his first race and Julie was going to ride him in the Open Ladies Race for the Shotestone Vase. Julie had been riding out on Master Johnson most days and had been doing twenty minutes skipping every morning to keep fit.

The farmers in the West Suffolk country had been invited by the Hunt as guests for the day. They had free admission to the special car park by the winning post and they were invited to the Farmers' Lunch. The lunch was a 'sit down' affair in the Farmers Luncheon Tent, which was located between the tote and the paddock.

Members of the Hunt Committee, some in striped aprons, served the lunch of cold meats, salad and baked potatoes. The carvers had been generous, and there were thick cuts of beef and ham with slice piled on slice and overlapping the enormous plates. Already on the tables were large jars of pickles and mustard and what appeared to be an unlimited kelter of bottles of beer with bottle openers lying alongside. The beer was donated by Sir Monty Biddlecombe, a regular follower of hounds, whose brewery owned over eighty 'tied' public houses in East Anglia.

Among those invited to the lunch was the Bishop who, to the considerable surprise of the Hunt Committee, had accepted the invitation.

There was, however, no table plan and the Bishop had unfortunately found himself sitting on the corner of one of the trestle tables where he was only able to converse with Sid Skinner, who could talk about nothing but horses. Sid had been an unsuccessful part-time trainer, and had now worsened in lifestyle to the menial task of leading horses round the ring at the monthly horse sales in Middlesham Market. Sid, a small dapper man, was wearing a dirty, mottled, yellow waistcoat and he had his napkin tied round his neck, like a child's bib.

The luncheon had gone off rather badly as Sid and the Bishop had little in common. At last, Sid thought he would talk about something in which he was sure that the Bishop would be interested. He said to the Bishop, "Do you know anything about Nebuchadnezzar?"

"Yes, Mr. Skinner," said the Bishop, "I can tell you quite a lot about him. In fact, he was the King of Babylon. What do you want to know?"

"I don't know nuthin' about the King of Babylon," said Sid, "but Nebuchadnezzar came from Ireland and I only want to know how long it took to get him fit when he came in off the grass."

"Oh," said the Bishop, "I'm afraid that I misunderstood you."

"Help yourself to some more beer then," said Sid, wiping his mouth with his sleeve.

*   *   *   *

Major William 'Brasso' Hawkins MFH stood on a bale of straw to make his speech in which he thanked the farmers who had allowed the Hunt to run over their land. It was not easy to hear what Major Hawkins said as he always held the microphone at considerable length as if it were a poisonous snake.

Sitting on the other side of Sid was 'Forky' Copeland. He was a one hundred and twenty acre, Irish bred, farmer from Stowmarket. He was a fat fellow with sticking out ears and a pendulous gut and had three bottles of beer inside him. He was always saying forkin' this and forkin' that. He said to Sid, "The forkin' Hunt ought to pay me ten bob an acre to come across my land. Last time they came round they broke a forkin' gate and let my sheep out, some of the old ewes were heavy in lamb an' all. None the more for that," said Forky, after a second thought, "I dew loike to see the owd Hunt about."

*   *   *   *

Out in the paddock area there were backers and bookmakers and a milling crowd of touts, tarts and farmers. The bookies were calling the odds on the first race, and also on the three o'clock, big handicap race in far away Exeter. They were ready to take bets on the Grand National which was only seven days away.

Julie was due to ride Master Johnson in the Ladies' Race at three o'clock and the horse, looking remarkably fit and well, had already arrived. Happy Tattersall, who had put on a collar and tie for the occasion, was walking Master Johnson round the horse box parking area.

During the early morning, Julie and I had walked the course. The fences had been built by the Cheltenham course builder and they were very firm indeed. To hit the top could make a horse spin.

*   *   *   *

Over in the special ten pound car park, the racegoers were laying out lunch behind the cavernous boots of their cars and the open doors of their hatchback shooting brakes. They removed from the baskets and hampers their gilded nosebags to display their triumphant spread.

Rachel and Clara, the two pretty Capel sisters from Langley Park, were there in tow with Twiston Rudd and Rodney Wilkes-Booth, two young bloods from the Stock Exchange. The party had arrived in Rodney's 1922 Bentley with its GB plates and a built-in drinks cabinet. They needed no lessons in social one-upmanship.

Clara was the cleverer of the two sisters and was in her last term at Benenden. Her parents had hoped that she would read history and economics at university and were aghast when she announced that she was going to do sociology and peace studies. Rachel, on the other hand, was the prettier of the two clean-bred sisters, but she was rather unimaginative and something of a mental plodder. She would be sent off to do cooking and secretarial training at a place for young ladies near Cheltenham. The hope would then be that she would meet a suitable young man before she was twenty.

They were joined by Monty Bolton of Hopstead Manor and Cecil Fanshawe of Belgrave Square SWI. Monty and Cecil were, according to Julie, the two biggest twerps in the South of England.

Monty affected a straw hat with a Guards Club hatband and equipped himself with a monocle as an essential architectural feature. Monty, who wore a single gold ear-ring, was a public school dropout and had a job at Lloyds. He had been brought up by nannies in Gloucestershire and London and he was said to possess the slowest mind in the City.

Cecil, on the other hand, considered himself to be something of a 'would be' poet. He had embarked on a lifestyle beyond his means and he had a great propensity for running into debt. He was definitely not in the healthiest shape financially. His father had been very rich, lost all his money and shot himself. Cecil, currently, was madly in love and sighed obsessively for a talentless actress named Cordelia Bone. Sadly for Cecil, he was very much a back number, Cordelia had shacked up with a married stagehand when she was in pantomime at Colchester. Cecil, who was wearing an orange shirt and a green and white spotted bow tie, and Monty had brought along with them Miss Virginia Blackett, still with her winter cruise tan.

Virginia, a lippy, petulant blonde educed an absence of humour and spoke with a certain intensity. She was wearing no stockings and her hair was held back by a wide green headband. She was said to wear black underwear and an expression of perplexity and she wouldn't eat inorganic cabbage or white bread.

The night before the Point to Point, Cynthia, Lady Fox, an indefatigable fixture on the London charity circuit, had organised a Young Persons' Ball. When Virginia had been introduced to Monty she had gushed, "I feel I have known you for absolute ages." And when she went home and told her mother about having met Monty she had said, "He's awfully interesting and frightfully clever." When Monty had telephoned that very morning and invited her to the Point to Point she was said to be 'frightfully bucked'.

Virginia had been 'finished' in Paris and although she had been taken to The Louvre and the Opera and had learned a few harmless expressions of colloquial French, what Virginia really wanted was a nice young man. She was hoping that the evening of the Point to Point would lead to amatory exploits and, at the thought of this, she slipped out her powder compact and began to titivate.

Monty had boasted that he had an uncle who was on the Trainers' Licensing Committee of the Jockey Club. Everyone knew, of course, that the Jockey Club, like the Kennel Club, was a law unto itself and was an autocracy with whom it was deemed imprudent to take liberties. Monty had once owned a horse called 'Driven Speed' which had cost him six thousand pounds at the Newmarket Yearling Sales. It had been entered for the Derby. Monty had fantasised that, resplendent in top hat and tails, he would lead in his winning Derby winner, to the acclaim of the Epsom multitudes. Instead of this, however, Monty had received a whopping great bill from his trainer and a surprisingly large one from the vet. Monty discovered that the bill included a hefty account from a chiropractor who the veterinary surgeon had recommended. It was hoped that he would be able to repair a suspected back problem by the removal of nerve interference by the manual adjustment of Driven Speed's spinal column.

In May of that year Driven Speed was entered in a five hundred and fifty pound novices race on the July course at Newmarket. The horse had finished last and his jockey had remarked that it was a useless animal. "It should", he said, "be put in cans." Monty had always said that his family had not owned a good horse since the sixth Duke of Portland had won the Derby. Why he said that was not clear as there was no connection whatsoever between Monty's family and that of the Duke of Portland.

*   *   *   *

The two Capel sisters lifted out the collapsible wooden table from the boot of the Bentley and spread a spotlessly white table cloth. The salmon and venison pate was then unpacked from the cold box. In the meantime, one of the young Stock Exchange blades uncorked a bottle of Moet Chandon and when he poured a rather full glass for his friend, the other young blade said, "I say, old chap, steady on. Got to go careful. I've got a dashed important engagement this evening – Samantha's coming out."

This was to be no common repast of beer and tomato sandwiches but, as Clara had remarked, "Beer and sandwiches are awfully good for people not like us." This comment marked her out as a girl of very superior culture and we can be sure that very few of us would be considered to be worthy of occupying a fitting position in their refined and polished circle.

Monty owned, in addition to his house in Belgrave Square, a cottage in Devon and a flat in Marbella. He was an Hon and the second son of an hereditary Peer of the Realm. He was part and parcel of the privileged dying aristocracy who were weaving some kind of conspiracy against progress. He had earned his spurs, early on, by stealing a policeman's helmet, in the Tottenham Court Road, and by nicking a lobster from Fortnum and Mason. Both episodes had received honourable mention in "Jennifer's Diary."

His eldest sister, Pussy, a tender young goddess, was doing her finals at Edinburgh. During the vacation on an organised shoot, Pussy, who was somewhat short-sighted had shot a cow in the best pheasant wood. It was remarked in *Private Eye* that there were no recriminations, not only because of Pussy's fine breeding, but also Pussy had honestly thought that the cow was a poacher!

So many were her virtues which became her birth and station.

*   *   *   *

Master Johnson, draped in his dark blue New Zealand rug, with yellow piping, was sweating and restless when he was led out of his box, but he had now settled down under Happy's soothing care.

Julie never ate any lunch when she was racing and I had no appetite either. I was worried about Julie and I was also worried about the horse. I was getting quite edgy and feeling rather like I did in the desert during the last hour before firing a three hundred round per gun nighttime barrage with twenty five pounders.

Time seemed to move slowly. Master Johnson hadn't run in a point to point before but he had been galloped over fences once a week with other horses and he had had a real pipe opener every Saturday morning. Master Johnson was very fit, and we were quietly confident that he had a reasonable prospect of finishing in the first three.

Every morning at 8.00am Happy Tattersall had supplied Master Johnson with his breakfast of nine pounds of corn, laced with garlic honey. Happy swore by garlic honey. "It's a damned sight better," said Happy, "than them owd condition powders what's advertised in the *Horse and Hound*." Master Johnson's dinner at 6.00pm consisted of another nine pounds of corn accompanied by bran, molasses and blood salts. On Wednesdays and Saturdays he was treated to a hot cooked bran and linseed mash which Master Johnson would push with his muzzle round his manger, waiting for it to cool down. The horse knew where his food came from and he would hummer and blow through his nose whenever Happy came into the yard. Master Johnson had been part of our life. We had lived with him, schooled him over fences, long reined him over logs in a circle, and now Julie was going to race him and share dangers with him.

The first race of the day was for horses owned by members of the West Suffolk Hunt and they had to be ridden by the owner or a member of his family. There were five runners and only two finished. Pussyfoot, owned by Jim Threadgold, a hunting grain merchant, and ridden by his son, Simon, was hot favourite, started at six to four on and, although carrying 14lbs extra, won by twenty lengths. It had certainly not been an exciting finish and as Peter said, 'there was no need to call for a photograph' and little had been missed by those members of the crowd that had been dallying over their lunch.

After the 2.15pm race the bookies settled down to make their book on the Ladies' Race and were shouting the odds.

I always tacked up Julie's horses. There is, of course, much more to saddling up a horse than slapping a saddle on his back.

Happy Tattersall stood at Master Johnson's head and held him by the bridle. Peter was there to give me a hand.

First, I put on the elasticated breast-girth and ran the strap over the horse's neck and later on attached the two ends of the girth to the main girth on the saddle. To further assist against saddle slip, a damp piece of chamois leather was laid across the horse's back. Over the leather was placed a lightweight pad of polythene which acts as a buffer to the saddle and helps to provent saddle sores. Peter then handed me the light cotton cloth bearing Master Johnson's race number and next I placed the weight cloth which contained six pounds of lead in the small leather pockets.

I then lifted on the lightweight racing saddle which was held in place by the girth. Over everything I tightened up a webbing surcingle which runs round the top of the saddle and is anchored under the horse's belly.

The paddock area was thronged with people. It was generally assumed that, as Master Johnson had not raced before and had no form, Julie was just going to hunt him round and show him the course. Hunter Rowe, the course commentator was announcing the names and numbers of the ten runners. The race was an open one and horses had come from all parts of the country, including an unknown, mysterious five year old, from Yorkshire. The winner would receive the prestigious Shotestone Vase, an enormous engraved and adorned silver cup presented by Sir Alan Stuart-Smith, the chairman of the Harwich and East Coast Shipping Company.

*   *   *   *

Back at the farm I still had in the silos a thousand tons of wheat which had not yet been sold from the last harvest. A good dry sample of feed wheat was making just over one hundred pounds a ton. I had decided therefore, to put 'a ton of wheat' on Master Johnson. I had asked Sally to put the money on for me and she had managed to get a price of ten to one. When Sally handed ten, ten pound notes to Harry Hodges, an old established bookie, the two tic-tac men standing on beer crates in front of the bookies, were suddenly jerked to life and within seconds the whole line of bookies had shortened Master Johnson's price to seven to one and later to six to one.

The hot favourite was Magic Ring, unbeaten this year and ridden and owned by the Hon. Jocelyn Lansbury. Jocelyn Lansbury was a hard-faced, sour looking woman with pushed-up hair. Magic Ring had already won two ladies' races this season and although he had opened up at six to four, it was now difficult to get even money on him.

Another fancied horse was Hullabaloo from the Old Surrey and Burstow. Hullabaloo was a large, washy chestnut with flaxen mane and tail, and was owned by Henry Kibble, a wealthy car breaker from Guildford. Henry was a rough diamond, but he thought the world of his eighteen year old daughter, Lucy, and he was determined that Lucy should be mounted on the best horse he could afford. He bought Hullabaloo for a lot of money. The seven year old had already won a couple of point to points in the West Country. The bookies were making Hullabaloo second favourite at five to two. Number seven was Devon Point, blinkered and wearing bandages on his front legs and boots for protection against an overreach. Devon Point had a distinct cough and it was unlikely that he would make three and a half miles.

It was generally expected that the short priced favourite, Magic Ring, would walk it.

Julie was standing in the paddock, whip in hand and looking neat and elegant in our racing colours of navy blue with white sleeves and blue and white quartered cap. She was easily the best looking girl in the ring and it was not unknown for some racegoers to have a saver on the prettiest jockey!

Peter and I stood with Julie in the centre of the ring. Master Johnson was in high feather and full of himself. He was all wire and whipcord without an ounce of surplus fat on him and he was prancing and tossing his head as Happy Tattersall proudly led him round the paddock.

Sally, together with the Ames and the Fosketts who had no doubt had a little flutter on Master Johnson, were standing some ten yards away up against the chestnut paling paddock fence.

"Good luck, Julie," said Jim.

Julie turned round and gave them a little wave. "Thanks Jim," she said, as she flapped her riding crop against her boots. I spotted a few people round the paddock from Newton Green. Some of them had come to give Julie support.

Archie Jolly was there with his cloth cap and his cheery red face. Lady Helena was there with her mother, a formidable, titled lady in brown check tweeds, with a blue silk scarf tied round her head. She had been striding purposefully through the crowd with racecard in one hand and handbag in the other.

*   *   *   *

The paddock steward rang the bell for the jockeys to mount and Happy brought Master Johnson over to us. Peter unbuckled the surcingle and the neck strap and eased the rug off the horse's back. Julie pulled on her yellow gloves. I tested the girths and tightened the straps up one hole and then pulled the irons down to the bottom of the shortened leathers. Happy held the restless Master Johnson and Julie gathered up the reins in her left hand and I gave her a leg up.

This was one of my worst moments as I knew that, even though the odds were a thousand to one, within ten minutes Julie could be lying out on the racecourse with a broken neck or unconscious, and under a horse used up in extreme fatigue, tired to exhaustion and weighing half a ton.

*   *   *   *

In the long history of steeplechasing there had been many serious accidents with jockeys being severely injured and even killed. Legs, arms, ribs and collar bones are frequently broken. One has to admire the professional jump jockeys and especially the less fashionable ones who, in order to get a living, have to ride bad horses. In a bad fall, a jockey can be kicked or rolled on by his own horse and jumped on and kicked by following horses. Perhaps the worst injuries, as the result of a fall, is the almost complete paralysis of the body from the neck downwards. All too frequently there can be splints, pins and screws in broken bones and other times there is severe brain damage.

So when Julie was racing I was always apprehensive and edgy. Only last year at Cottenham, a horse had run out at the first fence and taken two others with him. They all ended up in a terrible pile up which had put Nick Barnes, who had been a real thinking jockey in the world of point to point racing, into intensive care and his horse into the knacker's cart. Nick was not only kicked in the face but the surgeons had inserted a 15" pin to keep his thigh together.

*   *   *   *

The judges, a neighbouring MFH and a deaf Brigadier in trench coats and bowler hats, had climbed up the wooden steps and were now in the farm wagon at the winning post, testing out their field glasses.

The two Hunt Whips, immaculately turned out in their scarlet coats and on a matching pair of greys, led the ten runners from the paddock on to the racecourse. Once on the racecourse the horses were cantered up to the Start and were now circling the Starter, Major 'Peanuts' Becher-Fane. Major Becher-Fane was a military man in every sinew. His life had encompassed service in the Coldstream Guards and Military Intelligence. He was born into a distinguished service dynasty and was educated at Harrow and Sandhurst. He had been an active member of the Old Harrovians Tennis and Raquets Club. In earlier times he had been A.D.C. to the Commander in Chief, Sudan.

Many people thought that in spite of his long military record Major Becher-Fane was a bit of a frosty old windbag. In certain company he would hold forth on Poona Horse and Skinners Horse. He would run on about his service in India, and the pig sticking and the hunting of jackals in Peshawar. He would also tell of the time, as an assistant political agent on the North West Frontier, how, with seven soldiers, he had been sent to rescue a peer's son who was feared lost in the Khyber.

Major Becher-Fane, bowler hatted, portly and red faced sat on his well-mannered cob between the two yellow flags marking the Start.

The crowds had taken up their places of vantage. Peter and Sally had brought their hard-topped Land Rover and I joined them standing on the roof. From here, with our field glasses, we were able to see the whole of the course with the exception of two fences which were behind the bookies and the tote. The resplendent colours of the lady jockeys mingled and splashed in the afternoon sun.

*   *   *   *

The Major, having called the roll, rode his roan cob over to the yellow flag on the car park side of the course and sitting on his splendid mount he raised the white flag above his head.

"Get into line, ladies," he said, "and walk up."

Hullabaloo was playing up and turning round. Master Johnson was well into his bit and Julie required all her strength to hold him back.

The flag went down with the Major's, "Away you go." And they were off.

I had said to Julie, in the paddock, that she ought to let the others get ahead at the first as this was Master Johnson's first race.

Julie had replied, "Not much hope of that, Albert. I'll never be able to hold him in when the others are running and as I've heard you say more than once, 'You can give away weight but you can't give away ground'. I am going to do what I always do and try and be in front over the first and then you can keep out of trouble if any of the others should run out or refuse."

She was right, of course and it was a long run up to the first and when they were thirty yards from the fence Julie was two lengths clear. One of the great thrills in steeplechasing is to be galloping on a pulling horse up towards the first with thundering hooves and the rest of the field close up behind you. In that situation, for your horse to fall or refuse could be disastrous and you could have the rest of the field on top of you. I was relieved, therefore, when the commentator said, "They are all safely over the first."

Master Johnson had jumped the first like a stag, giving the fence plenty of daylight, and as they came to the second the commentator was saying, "Master Johnson is still two lengths clear."

They were now heading out into the country, and Peter, who was looking through his binoculars said, "They are all over the water and Magic Ring has moved up with Julie."

The commentator then said, "Firebird and Dazzling Gem were both fallers there."

Firebird was a hot, inexperienced five year old. He was a horse that liked to bowl along in front, but it was a job to keep him straight. In fact, he had taken Marcia Foster, who had lost a pedal at the water, right through the wing of the fence. Marcia had shot over his head and luckily had just missed hitting her head on the rails. Both the horse and rider were now up but Lucinda Grey and Dazzling Gem who had stuck his nose in the ground and had somersalted like a shot rabbit were still lying by the landing side of the fence and the red flag for an ambulance, and a yellow flag for the vet, were being vigorously waved by the St. John's men and the course steward.

Julie, and Jocelyn Lansbury, who was in yellow colours with black diamonds, were setting a cracking gallop with Lucy Kibble some two lengths behind. Julie was on the inside and going the shortest way. These three were now well clear of the rest as they turned the corner at the top of the hill, leaving the red flag on the left. Julie, and Jocelyn Lansbury took the fence coming on to the racecourse together, with Hullabaloo, making ground on the inside, only a length behind, and trying to get into the firing line. They galloped up the course with thundering hooves and were soon racing through the crowd and past the winning post for the first circuit. Julie never moved and Master Johnson, with ears pricked and full of running, was beginning to force the pace, but there was still a long way to go and Hullabaloo, now wide on the outside, was moving up. The fancied Yorkshire horse was back marker.

A minute later the commentator was saying, "There's nothing between the leaders as they go for the water."

Peter said, not taking his binoculars from his eyes, "They are really motoring now. I think that Julie can win this, Albert." My heart was pounding like I'd had a live rabbit for breakfast.

As they turned at the top of the hill it was clear that Hullabaloo was tiring and that the race lay between Master Johnson and Magic Ring. As they raced towards the third last, the commentator said, "Mrs. Lansbury and Julie Cooper are jumping stride for stride and have gone into overdrive."

I heard a bookmaker shout, "Six to four Magic Ring."

"Someone thinks that Master Johnson is winning," said Peter.

Halfway down the hill they were still neck and neck and as they jumped the second last the commentator said, "This is a hell of a race but Mrs. Lansbury has got her whip out and Magic Ring is under pressure."

"A good sign," said Peter, quietly, "and Magic Ring met that fence a fraction close."

Julie began to push Master Johnson, she touched her whip on his shoulder and drove him into the last. Julie knew that at the end of a long steeplechase and even when winning easily, a jockey should never let the horse down and she was riding the finish as if her life depended on it. Master Johnson was showing a tremendous turn of foot.

"I reckon the Lansbury horse is cooked," said Peter. But Magic Ring had plenty of fight in her and the crowd were cheering this tremendous finish. Magic Ring got within half a length of Master Johnson but in the last hundred yards Julie, riding for all she knew, began to pull away and Master Johnson found the stamina and staying power needed to keep in front and to win in terrific style by a length and a half.

Julie loosened her hold on the reins, pushed back her racing goggles, then trotted Master Johnson right out. Fred Sayers had given Julie the old trainers' tip, and said that many good horses had started a breakdown by being pulled up too sharply after a hard finish.

It had been a tremendous race and Jocelyn Lansbury brought Magic Ring up beside Julie and said, "Congratulations, Mrs. Cooper. I'm afraid poor old Magic Ring had nothing left at the end and didn't get the distance."

I jumped down off Peter's Land Rover and hurried to the winning post. Happy Tattersall, wreathed in smiles, was already there and was waiting for Julie to come back to the gate so that he could lead her in. I could see Julie's head above the admiring crowd and forced my way through. "Well done, darling," I said, patting her earth-spattered boot.

"He gave me a super ride," said Julie, smiling.

Happy seized the bridle and snapped on the lead rein and led Master Johnson, with steaming coat and flecks of froth, into the winner's stall in the unsaddling enclosure. There was a little burst of applause as Julie was led in. She swung her leg over and slid down from the saddle. The Fosketts and the Ames were already there, thrilled to be friends of the winning owner and jockey.

"Did you have a bet?" I said to Stuart.

"We all did," said Stuart, "and we have won nearly a hundred between us. We're all suffering from nervous exhaustion. Julie rode an absolute blinder."

Julie undid the girths and pulled off the saddle and weight cloth and I followed her into the weighing tent where she sat on the scales. The pointer moved round to ten stone.

"O.K. Julie," said Dennis Wharton, who was Clerk of the Scales and Master of the North Essex Drag.

Julie had won the Ladies' Open and was queen for the day.

Sally came in. "What shall I do about your betting ticket," she said, "I'm not keen on collecting all that money."

I had nearly forgotten that I had given Sally a hundred to put on Master Johnson. "Did you get tens?" I asked.

"Yes," said Sally, brightly.

"Good Lord," I said, "who is it with?"

"Harry Hodges," said Sally.

"Oh, he's all right," I said, feeling more relaxed than I had done since early morning. "I'd better take the ticket and go and see him, if you will look after Julie."

When I reached Harry Hodges' pitch he had just removed the rubber band from a wad of used fivers and he said, "You really put it across me then, Albert. Why did you do it all with me?"

"Well Sally tells me that you were at tens when everyone else was eights and nines," I said.

"I managed to lay half of it off," said Harry. "You'll have to take a cheque."

"That's all right, Harry," I said.

So Harry Hodges wrote me out a cheque for eleven hundred pounds. "You won't get ten to one on Master Johnson again," he said.

It soon got round that I had won a thousand pounds on Master Johnson, and it was thought, in some circles, that we had been planning a betting coup, but that would have been something of an exaggeration.

*   *   *   *

On the way home, with the enormous silver cup wrapped in a rug on the back seat of the car, Julie said, "You know the big bay horse that was hot favourite for the fourth race and came about fourth."

"Yes," I said, "he came up from Kent."

"Well," said Julie, "before the race I was in the weighing tent, and I heard the owner, that horsy-looking fellow in a pork pie hat and a yellow pullover, say to the jockey, 'Get as close as you can but don't give him a hard race'."

"You know what that means," I said.

"I presume," said Julie, "that it means in so many words, 'don't win'."

"Of course it does," I said, "it is worth a packet to a bookie to know that a favourite isn't trying so that he is able to lay against it."

"I didn't think that this went on in point to points," said Julie.

"Yes," I said, "I shouldn't be surprised if a small minority don't give the horses drugs to slow them down and 'hurry up' pills when they are out to win. The authorities are not as strict with testing at point to points as they are for National Hunt racing. You may not have noticed that Raymond Frith's horse, Blue Devil, that won the open by six lengths had a starting price of six to one. That horse has run at Cottenham, Higham and Horseheath this season and hasn't finished in the first three."

"I would have thought that would result in a stewards' enquiry," said Julie.

"Well, it didn't today," I said, "and many people are under the impression that Raymond can win with Blue Devil whenever he wants to."

CHAPTER THIRTY
The Harvest Thanksgiving

Julie put down the phone and shouted excitedly, "Albert, the Bish is coming."

"What?" I said. "Who's the Bish?"

"The Bishop, stupid," said Julie.

"Is he coming here?" I asked.

"He's not only coming here," said Julie, "but he's coming for lunch after the Harvest Festival, together with the Vicar, two Churchwardens and Molly Bassett-Palmer."

"Good Lord," I said, "how long before the Harvest Festival?"

"Three weeks today," said Julie, "you've got plenty of time to get the lawns cut and the garden tidied up."

"Why do you think that the Vicar has decided to bring the Bish here?" I said.

"I expect that we have been honoured because you have been asked to be a J.P. and are a general Lord Tom Noddy."

"Much more likely because you are the Vice Chairman of the Flower Club," I said.

"Chairperson, if you don't mind," said Julie.

"Chairperson, my foot," I said, "that's a load of codswallop. What's wrong with 'Madam Chairman'?"

"You are a male chauvinist pig," said Julie.

"If you call me that again I shall have to give you a big cuddle," I said.

"You are a big, fat, ugly, chauvinist pig," said Julie.

*   *   *   *

It was the day of the Newton Green Harvest Thanksgiving and the Bishop would be giving the sermon.

The old Norman church, with the morning sun streaming through its windows, had its power of fascination, and was dressed overall in floral splendour. The yellow harvest sheaves blended with its polished wood and burnished brasses. Brightly coloured hips and haws lined the choir stalls.

The Bishop, who it was said always travelled First Class and stayed Five Star, was a bulky man whose waistcoat buttons were under considerable tension. He had thin, white hair and big fingers. It was said that he enjoyed his food and he certainly carried an excess of belly timber and his trousers pinched him round the middle.

He was a man of liberal principles and he belonged to the classical culture framework. At Oxford he had gained a First in Classics and was awarded his D.D.

145

while in his thirties. He had a good brain and had always been determined never to use the Ecclesiastical Library for his sermons. None the less his deep respect for tradition led him to be sharply critical of some of the lesser clerics with their modish and fashionable theologies. He had enough on his plate with the trendy agenda liberals and the Bible-bashing evangelists, whose numbers were increasing alarmingly. He was also concerned at the increasing desire of some of the clergy for new parochial independence and with what he considered the new increasing domination of affairs by the laity. He suffered vexation and despair at the clumsy, bungling incompetence of State intervention.

He was devoted to the scriptural teachings and the doctrine of worship set out in the Book of Common Prayer and he strongly upheld the Authorised Version. There were those who believed that a certain lack of energy prevented his full potential from being fulfilled, and there were those who considered that the Bishop should spend more time each month in the parishes with the clergy and less on the committees in Westminster. However, all who came under his influence were made aware of life's deeper spiritual dimensions.

The Bishop, in his vestments which had been washed and ironed by the ladies of the Cathedral, wearing his conical shelled mitre on his head and carrying his pastoral staff, passed through the full pews of the congregation, following the church choir and the Reverend Quartius Trussel into the precincts of the Chancel.

*   *   *   *

The beauty of the flowers in the church won golden opinions and resounded to the honour of the ladies in the Village to whom, over the years, demonstrators in the Flower Club had instructed in focal point and shape and colour.

Not everything, however, was sweetness and light among the blooms. Mrs. Vera Cox, an exceedingly sharp woman with mousy hair, thoroughly agreed with Mrs. Miriam Sidebottom, a nervous, jumpy woman, who that very morning had finished putting the fringe on her latest lampshade, that the arrangement of Mrs. Bull by the Altar was far too crowded and the foliage was too heavy. "What is more," said Mrs. Sidebottom, "it clashes with your arrangement, Mrs. Cox."

"I thought," said Mrs. Cox, with tedious worthiness in every fibre, "that we said yellow, brown and bronzes."

The dove of peace rested uneasily on the breasts of the church flower arrangers.

*   *   *   *

The Bishop was deeply aware that in the villages the Church followed the plough, and his sermon ranged over the farming year and its amazing reproductive cycle – ten fold, an hundred fold, stony ground and all that.

From his position in the pulpit the Bishop could look down on the 13th Century octagonal font, carved from oolite limestone which had been quarried in Barnarch in Northamptonshire, centuries ago. Leaning on the font were two half bags of King Edward potatoes, three sheaves of yellow Huntsman wheat and two tins of

V. Kneale.

baked beans. As the bounty at the harvest service was destined for the home for unmarried mothers in Middlesham, Josh Hobday, who had an allotment, had decided to contribute the baked beans instead of his usual pound and a half of runners. Josh considered that the tins of baked beans would require less preparation and cooking and so would prove to be more acceptable to the unmarried mothers. The Bishop also observed, lying on the floor across the base of the font like a stranded shark, Ephraim Small's usual absurd, enormous, useless marrow.

The Bishop, to indicate to us that he was with us heart and soul and not without humour, told the story of the man who said there were two things you never saw. The first was a dead donkey and the other was a poor farmer. This little pastoral homily raised a titter among members of the congregation that were envious members of the professions and also among the lower orders of rustic chaff in the Village.

Will Potter, a thirty acre smallholder who hadn't been to church since Easter and who considered himself a very poor farmer indeed, decided, as a measure of retaliation and protest at the lack of recognition of his poverty, that his contribution to the offertory would now be half a crown instead of the ten shilling note that reposed in his trouser pocket.

* * * *

We were eleven for lunch. The Bishop and his wife arrived in their black chauffeur driven Daimler. Thomas, the chauffeur-valet, had packed the Bishop's vestments into an old, worn, red suitcase. After shepherding the Bishop and his wife up to the front door, the chauffeur directed himself to the kitchen door where Ted's wife, Mrs. Kettle, who had been keeping an eye on the cooking while we were at church, was soon welcoming Thomas with half a wine glass of dry sherry.

The Vicar and Mrs. Trussel followed in their old 12hp Vauxhall. The car, saturated in age and mileage, was rather thirsty and this was duly noted at the last meeting of the Parochial Church Council. The Vicar's petrol, telephone and postage were paid out of a special fund which relied mainly on the interest on a sizeable capital gift which had been left to the Church by a wealthy benefactor. The donor of this benefaction had now lain in the ostentatious family vault in the churchyard, which outrivalled the other memorials, for over one hundred years.

We had invited to the lunch with the Bishop and his wife, Peter and Sally, Miss Millicent Cope and Norman Pennyfeather, the two Churchwardens and Molly Basset-Palmer, who enthusiastically played the organ and was often some way ahead of the congregation.

Peter, Sally and Molly Basset-Palmer could be relied on to keep the conversation flowing and I told Sally to go easy on the Bishop, and not to imagine that she was having a free for all at the University Debating Society.

"Oh," said Sally, "I was hoping to ask the Bishop if he was in favour of marrying gay couples."

"Don't you dare," I said, "it might give the old boy a heart attack."

I had done a bit of homework and although it was traditional that there should be clerical leanings towards the sherry decanter I knew that the Bishop's favourite tipple was elsewhere. I quietly asked him if he would prefer a whisky and soda. The Bishop caught me by the arm and said, "Dear boy, perhaps a little one, I mustn't overdo it as I have two more services today."

Sally, in a high-necked blouse and who was tall, pretty and bright, was soon engaging the Bishop in conversation. Sally knew that the Bishop was a caring Bishop and that he sat in the House of Lords. She also knew that he ran in the mainstream of traditional orthodox Christianity. You could say that he was a saintly man and that his burden compared with that of a Captain of Industry in these days when too few parsons were chasing too few livings.

Sally, in smoky-coloured tweeds and a blue silk scarf, had an instinct for asking pertinent questions and the capacity to stir controversy. "Tell me, Bishop," she said, "how many bishops are there in the House of Lords?"

"Twenty six," said the Bishop, with his hands behind his frock-coated back, "but most of them are seldom there."

"Do any of the Catholic bishops sit in the Lords?" asked Sally, innocently.

"Good gracious, no," said the Bishop, who had long learned to tolerate the doctrinal eccentricities and personal extravagancies of senior and junior clerics as well as from members of the laity. "The Church of England looks after its own, as indeed does The Church of Rome."

"And who selects the Bishops?" enquired Sally, gaily.

"Bishops are nominated by the Sovereign and then elected by The House of Bishops."

"So then," said Sally, "you elect yourselves."

The Bishop maintained that thoughtful silence which is the correct posture to observe in the graver crises of life and knowing that the Church's express purpose was to infuse charity, gentleness and wisdom into modern society, smiled a smile of benign complacency at the attractive, slim, young farmer's wife. He said, "There probably is room for change in the democratic foundations of The Church of Englandland and its relations with the State."

Sally knew that the previous month the General Synod of The Church of England had travelled to York for its annual summer outing. It had been a residential session at the York University. Some sceptical clerics hung in doubt and considered the Synod to be an horrendously expensive white elephant. When Sally mentioned this the Bishop said, with a wry smile, "There is a school of thought that considers too much importance is attached to the The General Synod and it has been suggested that deliberations of The General Synod should perhaps be conducted no more frequently than once in every ten years."

*   *   *   *

Our nine guests seemed to enjoy their lunch and became quite chatty. In fact, Molly Basset-Palmer, who had only had two sherries, and her first glass of wine, became very chatty indeed and chipped in with comments of little consequence, and indulged in giggles of delightful discomposure. It was providential that she was not required to play the organ at a service in the early afternoon, as at this particular moment in time she was full of trivial talk.

Sally had done two enormous bowls of flowers and Mrs. Kettle had highly polished the long oak table and the place settings gleamed.

Julie had cooked half a dozen young partridges to perfection. They were crisp outside and moist inside and they were garnished with watercress and served with bread sauce and game chips.

The previous day Julie had said to me, "What wine are you going to serve with the partridges?"

"I've no idea," I said. "Red, I suppose."

"You'll have to do better than that," said Julie, *The Good Food Guide Book* is on the shelf and it'll give you some ideas."

I took the book off the kitchen shelf and opened it at the 'Partridge and Pheasant' chapter. "Are they highly seasoned?" I asked.

"Yes," said Julie, "no end of herbs and things have gone into the stuffing."

"Well, it says here that it needs a robust wine."

"Robust?" said Julie, "I didn't know that a wine could be robust."

"I think they mean 'heavy'," I said, "They recommend here a Rhone wine or a Chateau Neuf du Pape."

"You'd better get three bottles of that, then" said Julie, "but I thought that Chateau Neuf du Pape was bottled in Ipswich."

"You could be right," I said, "but I think that we'd better go round and see what they've got in the supermarket."

So on the Saturday morning Julie and I had popped round to the huge store in Middlesham, and stood before the shelves of wine. There was a printed notice on one of the special shelves and it read 'Each wine is chosen for its character and expression of the region, reflecting the personality of the maker'. A wine from The Loire was described as 'being steeped in the wild savagery of the landscape'. "That is absolute tosh," said Julie.

"This one," she said, picking up a bottle of German Nierstein, "was mentioned by the wine buff in the Sunday paper."

"What did it say?" I asked.

"It said," said Julie, replacing the bottle on the shelf, "that it is an unpretentious little wine."

"What the hell is that supposed to mean?" I said. "It looks to me as if we would be safer with this one. It says on this label that it is ideal with poultry, meat, fish or salads, and underneath it says 'To be enjoyed at any time'."

"That covers practically everything except partridges," said Julie, "I think all this waffle is a confidence trick."

"Of course it is," I said. "Did you see in one of your women's magazines the other day that they were saying that one of the Italian wines was 'an amusing little wine'?"

"All wines are amusing, if you drink enough of it," said Julie, "I think that we had better stick to the old Chateau Neuf du Pape. It says on the label that it's from a noble grape variety, and it's a bit more expensive than some of the others. It also says that the Chateau Neuf du Pape is soft and well balanced with a tangy floral bouquet whereas this plonk over here is described as plummy with gentle hints of spice."

"I don't know," I said, "why people don't find a wine they enjoy and then stick to it instead of this yanking about with all these mysterious labels everytime they come in looking for something to impress their friends. Quite honestly, compared with some of this plonk, Mrs. Tattersal's elderberry wine is a classic and her dandelion and mangel goes with everything from rabbit to fish fingers."

As we placed three bottles in the trolley, I said, "Let's stick this wine in that heavy old decanter that your mother gave us for Christmas and then they will think it is all plonk and that we are trying to hide the labels."

For the pudding Julie had concocted a dish with oranges and chocolate with a considerable content of Cointreau and plenty of whipped cream. It was one of Sally's recipes and the Bishop's wife and Norman Pennyfeather, who wished the PCC could afford a Flymo for the churchyard, and Molly Basset-Palmer all had second helpings.

Mrs. Kettle brought in the coffee.

*   *   *   *

Julie had been quite nervous beforehand but when the guests had all gone she said, "Well, that seemed to go off all right."

"Yes," I said, "and I think that the Bish enjoyed his lunch."

"Yes," said Julie, putting the cream back in the fridge, "he's a dear old boy and he's got to preach another sermon this afternoon and one in Christchurch this evening. Do you think he preaches the same sermon in all three churches?"

"Of course he does," I said, "and his poor wife will have to hear, all over again, about no-one ever having seen a dead donkey or a poor farmer."

"He's sixty nine," said Julie "and I bet he'd like to put his feet up instead of traipsing round to two more churches this afternoon."

"That's a nice thought," I said, "I think I'll put my feet up for half an hour."

" Oh no you won't," said Julie, throwing me a dry tea cloth with the emblem of The National Trust and prints of furry badgers all over it. "I have sent Mrs. Kettle home and you can start with the wine glasses. And be careful."

I caught the tea cloth and said, "I'm fed up with all this hoo hah about badgers, pretty little fox cubs and bloody pandas. The pandas won't breed, the foxes kill our chickens and the badgers in the sett at the bottom of Hopcroft are ruining half an acre of wheat where they chase each other around the District. They reckon they're at bloody Silverstone."

"Don't you dare talk like that when Mrs. Curtis-Finch or any of her anti-farmer, hedgehog loving friends are around," said Julie, "you'll be hung, drawn and quartered."

"Well," I said, "they will stop hunting and within ten years there will be no pheasants or partridge or songbirds left and the countryside will be lousy with foxes and magpies."

"Don't exaggerate," said Julie.

Julie pulled on some rubber gloves and poured washing-up liquid into the bowl of hot water. I picked up a wine glass from the draining board and said, "I don't mind drying up but I don't like putting away."

"I don't think you've ever done it," said Julie. "Perhaps one day we'll have a dishwasher."

"It's not worth it," I said, "just for two."

"Sally's got one," said Julie, placing another wine glass on the draining board.

"I might consider it," I said, "if you can find a dishwasher where all the parts are made in England and it is assembled in England, but I am not letting you have a German or an Italian dishwasher just so that you can be one up on Mrs. Curtis-Finch."

CHAPTER THIRTY-ONE
The Ploughing Match

The first Saturday in October was the day of the Middlesham Farmers' Club Ploughing Match. The Match was to be held on the High Sheriff's off hand estate at Burnham Hall. The site was ideal. It was a ninety acre field, right beside the main road.

By 8 o'clock the morning sun had forced through its pencils of morning brightness and flushed fine sprays of light along the edges of the grey stones on the wall of the churchyard. The path leading up to the church door lay under a rug of small leaves and a blush of reddening fire was breaking light in the east in the continuation of the rapidly rising day.

*   *   *   *

The Ploughing Match Committee had elected Peter Henderson as their Chairman.

At 9 o'clock on the previous morning, in short wheel-based pickups and Land Rovers, eight members of the Ploughing Match Committee, dressed in Barbour jackets and gum boots and carrying marking pegs and measuring tapes, had turned up on the site to mark out the stetches. The tractor drivers, with their tractors and ploughs, had been arriving on the site since dawn. The number of each stetch was stencilled on white cardboard squares pinned onto a wooden marking peg. As the competitors arrived they were shown to their plots by the stewards.

About half of the ploughs being used that day were manufactured by the internationally known ploughmakers, Ransome, Sims and Jefferies of Ipswich. Ransomes had been making ploughs for one hundred and fifty years and had exported ploughs all over the world. On this prime occasion they were presenting a magnificent Challenge Cup for the Champion Ploughman.

*   *   *   *

There were six individual ploughing classes, and for each class there were two judges. Some of the judges had travelled from neighbouring counties. Martin Salter had flown in, together with his co-judge, Everet Carter, in Martin's bright red helicopter.

It was half past nine and all forty nine tractors with ploughs hitched on were standing at the head of their plots. Peter stood on the tailboard of his Land Rover and using his loudhailer, called in all the competitors for a briefing. They stood around the Land Rover in clean overalls and cloth caps, hands in pockets. There were men there proficient, competent and hardened by the land. There were solid yeomen of the soil, keen-eyed, knowledgeable and with unsparing loyalties. These men were wise in their generation and masters of the ploughing craft.

*   *   *   *

"Right," said Peter, when all the competitors were gathered around, "Draw out your opening furrow and wait until the judges have seen it. There are twenty points for the opening split. Then," went on Peter, "head in three rounds and again wait until the judges have marked the head. And then split the rest of the land between your own work and the competitor on your left and don't forget that there are thirty points for general work and another thirty points for the shut out. Start when you are ready."

The ploughmen, many of them old hands at ploughing matches. calmly strolled back to their machines. There was no great hurry. They had already spent hours sharpening discs and shares.

Then the day burst into life as the self-starters were activated and there was the cough and roar of powerful engines. The drivers were focusing their eyes on the distant wooden peg at the far end of their plot for the opening furrow. The judges, with their clipboards and marking sheets, began to move along the headlands.

An almost invisible haze of steel blue smoke hovered over the end of the vertical muttering exhaust pipes.

*   *   *   *

Alf Bucket and 'Bumble' Small were working members of Bert Jepson's threshing gang. Alf cut the strings and threw the sheaves into the barnwork and Bumble was 'cavings' man. They both lived for the weekend and the beer. It was just after half past ten and they had already had a skinful. When they arrived at the Ploughing Match they were staggering unevenly between the ploughing stetches. Alf was

three parts cut, but he was the most sober of the two and he was doing his best to help Bumble who had already fallen over a couple of times on the headland.

"Yew know," said Bumble, leaning on Alf and with his cap over one eye, "Oi dew loike the owd Ploughin' Match."

"Yew steady up, me owd mate," said Alf, "can't hev yew a'fallin' over, yew moight git ploughed in."

"An' then," slurped Bumble, happily, "an' then yewd hev ter put manure on Oi."

Alf roared with laughter, "Oi reckon that'd make yer grow loike an owd mangel."

Ben Johnson, one of the stewards, in breeches, gum boots and deerstalker hat, drew up and said to Alf, "You'd better lay old Bumble down behind the tea tent, he might get run over."

"Tea tent! Tea tent!" repeated Bumble, "Oi dunt wanna goo nowhere near no bloody owd tea tent. Tea gives yer rot gut."

"Come on, Bumble, me owd mucker," said Alf, "Oi'll hev ter git yer set down on a bale a'straw do else yer'll keep fallin' over." But Alf was also in an advanced state of intoxication and when Bumble fell into a bed of nettles on the headland, Alf picked up an old corn sack and lay down beside him.

I was stewarding the four-furrow class and Tom Whittaker, our Committee Vice-Chairman, came along and said, "we can't leave those two old boys laying there in the middle of the Ploughing Match."

So we borrowed one of the demonstration tractors with a buck rake on the back and gently laid the two old stagers across the tines and carted them over to the hedge. We broke open a bale of straw and laid a tractor sheet on top and then laid Alf and Bumble, who was still snoring, on their bed and they slept the afternoon away. Alf and Bumble didn't see too much of the Ploughing Match but they could not have had a happier day. In fact, when they came to in the late afternoon, Alf said, "Yew know, Bumble, Oi was a'dreamin' Oi'd won the owd Ploughin' Match."

"Yew can't say that," said Bumble, "Yew can't drive a bloody tractor."

"Nobody can't never say that," said Alf, "Oi hent never troid."

*　　　*　　　*　　　*

The Champion Ploughman that day was fifty one year old Jim Wheeler. Jim had left his stretch in such good order with all rubbish buried and the furrows so well packed that one of the judges said, "It only wants a set of harrows over that and it will be fit for drilling."

Most of the tractors were British made Fordsons but Jim drove an American made, green painted John Deere tractor and was using a Swedish made Kverneland plough. Jim was head tractor driver for the Linton estates, an estate of seven farms in the North of the County.

At the prizegiving Jim, who had wiped the oil off his hands, removed his cap and walked up to receive the Championship Cup from Mrs. 'Boo-Boo' Philipa

Farquarson, the wife of the High Sheriff. Jim received an enthusiastic round of applause. He also picked up the cup for coming first in the Three Furrow Class, twenty pounds for driving a John Deere tractor and a silver watch for using a Kverneland plough. Jim had had a good day.

In the root and cereal classes, which were always held in conjunction with the Ploughing Match, Julie and I had won first prize for a sample of milling wheat and a second prize for half a dozen roots of sugar beet. The judge for the cereals was Henry Waters, a well-known seed merchant, and he said to me, running a handful of my wheat through his fingers, "Albert, if you have got fifty tons of this I could give you a tenner over feed wheat price." Henry Waters knew that my wheat would be free of wild oats and he wanted it for seed.

"When would you want it?" I said.

"I could send a couple of bulk lorries down next Monday."

"That'll be O.K." I said, "my forklift will load forty tons an hour so we shouldn't hold your lorries up for long."

Julie and the wives of the Ploughing Match Committee had had a busy day catering for the competitors, who were always given a free lunch, and also catering for the judges and the general public.

Julie said, that evening, "It's all very well for you old men on the Committee swanning about the field giving orders and sitting about on your shooting sticks, looking important, but for us poor old wives it's damned hard work."

"You know you all enjoy it," I said, "I've never heard so much chattering gibble gabble coming from the refreshment barn as there was when you women were laying the tables. A thousand starlings wouldn't have been able to make themselves heard."

"Watch it!" said Julie.

CHAPTER THIRTY-TWO
The Poultry

Our most profitable enterprise consisted of the production of day old chicks. There were some five thousand laying hens all out on free range and in half-acre wire netting runs. The cockerels to mate with our hens were purchased from some of the most famous poultry breeders in England. We brought in cockerels from the top breeding pens of Golden, Macintyre and Richard Rodwell and we thought nothing of paying five pounds for an egg from one of the top laying trial trap nested pens.

In the purpose-built hatchery stood three enormous Secura sixteen thousand egg incubators. Hatching day was always on a Tuesday, and the Japanese chick sexers would arrive at about five o'clock in the evening to sort out the sexes of the chicks. We were selling around five thousand day old pullets a week.

One of our main concerns with the incubators, was that it was necessary to guard against the effects of an electicity cut. If the fans stopped turning, the temperature in the incubators rose alarmingly and the eggs, worth over three thousand pounds, would be 'cooked'. An alarm was fitted to the incubator thermostats and if the temperature rose or fell more than one degree the alarm bell rang in our bedroom, at night. It was then necessary to turn on our petrol-driven auxiliary generators.

Peter Henderson came over to see our hatching enterprise, and we sat in the warm hatchery, while Sally and Julie nattered in the kitchen. We listened to the soft purr of the fans that were circulating the hot air over the eggs and through the machines.

Peter said, "How many hens did you say you had, Albert?"

"Around five thousand," I said.

"And so you must be collecting something like fifteen thousand eggs a week," said Peter.

"Well, I hope to get rather more than that," I said, "but we require fifteen thousand fertile eggs a week and then, reckoning to get at least one pullet from three eggs, I can book up to sell five thousand day old pullets a week."

"How much does it cost you to produce a hundred fertile eggs?" enquired Peter.

"It should set us back, taking into consideration the cost of the cockerels in the mating pens, no more than forty shillings a hundred."

"So the cost of the eggs to produce one hundred day old pullets, is six pounds."

"That's about it," I said, "and I sell the pullets at fifteen pounds per hundred and this goes up to twenty pounds per hundred in March and the only variable cost is for the electricty for the incubators and the charge for the sexing."

"According to my calculation," said Peter, "the poultry are making a clear profit of four hundred pounds a week."

"Well, some weeks we might take double that, but don't forget these day old pullets are only really wanted from January to June to fit in with the laying year and sometimes, if fertility is high and we have a really good hatch, we have a surplus of chicks. I also have the head poultryman and his two assistants to employ all through the year. There is always the risk that the flock could get 'fowl pest' or some other serious disease which could be near ruination and we also have a certain amount of fox trouble. Things may look fine in the Spring and Summer," I said, "but I don't think you would fancy feeding and watering five thousand hens out on free range when there is ten inches of snow on the ground and five degrees of frost. The water freezes as soon as it is put in the drinking troughs and without water the birds won't eat and go right off lay."

"I expect that you save a bit on sexing the chicks of the sex-linked breeds," said Peter.

"Yes," I said, "if we use a Rhode Island Red cockerel on a Light Sussex hen the resulting pullets come out brown and the cockerels come out white, so they sex themselves. However, we still have a long way to go in technology and special hybrids will be produced which will knock spots off our cross breeds, as far as egg production is concerned.

*   *   *   *

Nationally we were getting quite well known as producers of high class, reliable chicks and we advertised in the poultry papers and magazines. Orders were coming in from all over the country from as far as the north of Scotland. Julie spent most of Wednesdays delivering chicks in our specially ventilated van to various customers in East Anglia and also to the railway station. Every Wednesday morning a load of chicks were put on rail for delivery to various parts of the country. The chicks travelled surprisingly well in their specially ventilated boxes and deaths were rare. Customers were always phoned and told when to expect arrival.

We had a glossy catalogue printed with plenty of coloured pictures of our birds enjoying themselves out on free range. For some reason or other customers thought that if the eggs were from hens on free range, the chicks would be stronger and healthier than if bred from birds in deep litter poultry houses. Although we knew that this was a nonsense we continued to plug, in our advertising, the merits of the great outdoors and the feeding of grain to keep the birds' gizzards working.

We publicised in our catalogues the fact that our breeding flocks were kept out in large runs where they could eat the young grass and would catch and digest worms and insects. We did not publicise the fact that the sun doesn't shine all the time, and nothing looks more miserable out in the rain than a pen of wet, bedraggled hens. There was also the risk of salmonella when the rooks, starlings and sparrows flew in to feed with the free range hens. We recalled the time when a strong March gale lifted the roofs off two of the houses and the frightened birds huddled together for warmth. The next morning we found over three hundred dead birds, suffocated and trampled to death. But the worst time for free range birds and the poultry staff was in the Winter with snow and ice and frozens runs and water troughs. We encouraged visits by urban groups and parties of school children but they seldom wanted to see round our farm in the depths of Winter.

It was a cheerless early morning in the middle of March, and it was blowing and raining hard. It had been a very wet night and the clouds showed dull and stormy. Out in the near paddock the thick steam was rising from the reeking bodies of the cattle. It was 6.00am and this was the weekly delivery day for our day old chicks. Julie and I had had our breakfast of toast and tea. Helmet had been in the hatchery since 5.30am, and by 7 o'clock we had packed up four thousand day old pullets in brown cardboard boxes. Each box contained fifty newly hatched, fluffy, cheeping chicks. The Japanese chick sexers had been over the night before to segregate the cocks from the pullets. The chick sexers, who seemed able to sex about a thousand chicks an hour, claimed to achieve 98% accuracy, but we always stuck in an extra four chicks per hundred, doing our best to ensure that our customers would get at least a hundred pullet chicks for every hundred ordered.

At 7.00am Helmet loaded eighty boxes of chicks into our new Bedford van. We were very proud of our van which was painted in gleaming white with faint green piping. Julie had been in touch with Steve Sloane who had exhibited some wonderful pictures of geese and ducks at the exhibition of the Bury Fine Arts Society. Julie had asked Steve to paint, on the sides of the van, a picture of a magnificent Rhode Island Red cock with a black and white Light Sussex hen and, underneath, five chicks sticking their fluffy yellow heads out of a box. Steve had done a magnificent job, and the beautifully crafted painting had attracted much attention and was a superb mobile advertisement for our chicks.

Emblazoned on the sides of the van, in green and gold lettering, was BROADSHOTS DAY OLD CHICKS and neatly inscribed on the door was A.K. and J.D. Cooper, Broadshots Farm, Middlesham.

Julie was going to deliver the four thousand Black Leghorn x Rhode Island Red chicks. They were destined for Jason Bennett Farms of Lower Caxton.

Julie came out wearing a roll-neck yellow jumper, a tweed skirt and high leather boots. She climbed into the van. There was a faint smell of expensive perfume. "Mind how you go." I said, "Drive carefully."

"Don't worry," said Julie, "I should be back by one o'clock." She closed the van door, blew me a kiss and I waved her off.

*   *   *   *

It was just after two o'clock when Julie returned. I had been discussing chick orders for the next three weeks with Helmet, in the hatchery, when I heard the van outside. I went out to meet Julie. The day had changed from a wet and windy morning to a day of brilliant sunshine, and when Julie climbed out of the driving seat she took off her pair of jumbo sunglasses and gave me a little peck on the cheek and then we both went over to the farmhouse kitchen for a cup of tea.

I slid the heavy iron kettle across onto the hot plate of the Aga and fished a couple of mugs out of the cupboard. Julie had put her hand into her pocket and pulled out two thick wads of bank notes. "Eight hundred in readies," she said, "or rather seven hundred and ninety eight. I took two pounds out for groceries."

"What are you going to do with that?" I said, "put it under the bed?"

"No," said Julie, "it's going into the Bank, first thing in the morning."

The sunlight filtered through the roller blind and scattered on the floor. "You're worse than the tax inspector," I said, "and another thing. I can't have you going out to deliver chicks all tarted up. You are supposed to be going out to deliver chicks, not to pick up men!"

Julie lifted a hand and smoothed a stray lock of her hair. "Most of our customers are men," she said, "and if I am well turned out it will give a good impression of our business and I always want to be a credit to my husband."

"You don't have to go out all scented up with that pongy Miss Dior and looking like a hussy in the red light district," I said, lifting the heavy kettle off the stove and pouring the boiling water into the teapot.

"Well," said Julie, looking impish, like a naughty fairy, "I was able to make quite an impression today."

"What was that?" I said.

"At Jason Bennett Farms," said Julie.

"What happened at Jason Bennett Farms?"

"Well, the great Jason Bennett, who is the big wheel behind it all, came down himself to help me unload the chicks, and to help me put them under the hover."

Julie always liked to see the first five hundred safely under the hover to ensure that our chicks were going onto clean wood shavings, that the temperature under the hover was ninety two degrees and that the thermostat in the hover was working to half a degree.

"Nothing remarkable about that," I said, "you have put thousands of chicks under hovers."

"I know," said Julie, coyly, "but not with Jason."

"You surely didn't go snogging with Jason under the hover," I said.

"No," said Julie, "But he did ask me if he could take me out to dinner one weekend." Then she said mischieviously, "I don't think that Jason's wife understands him."

"I'll smash his face in," I said, "and what did you say?"

"I said that I would think about it," said Julie.

"You never did," I said, getting ever so slightly worried.

"No. Actually," said Julie, "I said that I didn't think my husband would like it and incidently, I shouldn't bother to smash his face in as Jason is six feet three and plays prop forward for Cambridge Wanderers."

"That was a daft thing to say," I said, somewhat relieved. "You probably missed out on a good dinner. Didn't Jason know who you were?"

"Well, I had my gloves on and I expect he thought I was your poultry girl, but it was very romantic in the brooder house."

"I'll give you romantic," I said, "You deserve to have your bot spanked with a hairbrush and next time chicks are delivered to Jason Bennett Farms, I'll send Helmet."

"Spoilsport," said Julie, "Helmet had better take his tank with him."

"Surely Jason wouldn't want to cuddle Helmet under the hover," I said.

"I wouldn't be surprised at anything these days," said Julie.

CHAPTER THIRTY-THREE
The NFU Annual General Meeting

There was the happy occasion when I went, with Peter, up to the Westminster Central Hall as a delegate to the NFU Annual General Meeting. Peter had been selected to propose the main composite resolution, in conjunction with the Yorkshire delegates, concerning 'The State of the Industry.

Julie and Sally came up with us and they had the day shopping. They spent most of the morning in the soft furnishings department of Peter Jones.

In the evening we all went to the NFU Annual Dinner at the Hilton. There were almost a thousand farmers, farmers' wives and distinguished guests at the dinner. Rural accents could be heard, among the boiled shirts and finery, from Sussex to Penrith and from the broadlands of East Suffolk to the hills of Aberystwyth. Among the distinguished guests were Sir Harold and Lady Macmillan, John Silkin and Mr. Fred Peart, the Minister and past Ministers of Agriculture. Our Chief guest and main speaker for the evening was the Prince of Wales.

These were heady times for British agriculture and when Prince Charles got up to speak the whole assembly rose and, for over two minutes, gave him a standing ovation. Some of the farmers' wives were standing on their chairs. Prince Charles seemed somewhat taken aback at this rousing reception before he had said a word of his speech.

When everyone had settled down, the Prince first of all said, "Are there any of my tenants here from the Duchy of Cornwall?" When two tables of Cornish farmers stood up and waved, Prince Charles said that if they could afford to come up and dine at the Hilton then he was charging them too little rent!

At the time of this dinner there had been public mention of a possible engagement of the Prince of Wales and he said that the media and many other people were trying to marry him off. The Prince had been talking to one of the farm workers on the Sandringham Estate and the farm worker had given Prince Charles certain advice. He had said, knowing that like begets like, "Master, afore you git married to any gals, you have a bloody good look at the mother."

When the top table retired after dinner it was to the loud and enthusiastic singing by a thousand farmers and their wives of *God Bless The Prince Of Wales*.

Afterwards, the Prince circulated among the guests. Peter, Sally, Julie and I were talking to Jim Patterson, our delegate to Headquarters, when the Prince came up and he said to me, "Where are you from?"

"West Suffolk, Sir," I said.

"I expect then you farm without livestock."

"No, Sir," said, "I keep ten thousand breeding hens and three thousand pigs."

"They must eat several tons of food a week," said the Prince, with a smile.

"Yes," I said, "the poultry eat eighteen tons of feed a week and the pigs just over fifty tons."

"Good Lord," said the Prince, "and I expect that you are using the computer-bred hybrids."

"Yes, Sir," I said, "we have our own elite breeding stock which has a high performance and a high health status and is monitored by the Pig Industry Development Authority."

"Have we caught up with the Danes as far as bacon quality is concerned?" he asked.

"Yes," I said, "the British bacon pigs are every bit as good and as lean as the Danes, but we sometimes criticize our curers for injecting too much brine into the sides of bacon in the curing tanks and this results in the bacon being too wet."

"They tell me," said the Prince, "that with pigs the ability to convert feed into meat is an hereditary factor."

"Yes," I said, "we call this the food conversion ratio, and all our breeding pigs have been tested for this factor. Ten years ago it required four pounds of feed to produce one pound live weight gain, but after ten generations of selective breeding we have been able to reduce this figure to three point three."

"I shall have to check up that our pigs on the Sandringham Estates are being monitored," said Prince Charles, as he moved off.

When Prince Charles had gone, Julie, who was always daft about Royalty, said, "Isn't he lovely?"

Julie was wearing a close fitting, low-cut, black velvet evening gown and her hair was piled up on top of her head. I caught her arm and said, "Darling, you are lovely too."

CHAPTER THIRTY-FOUR
The County Farm Competition

"Whoever could make two ears of corn or two blades of grassgrow
upon a spot of ground where only one grew before would deserve
better of mankind and do more essential service to his country
than the whole race of politicians put together."

Jonathon Swift

The following year Julie and I decided to enter our farms in the County Farm
Competition which was run and organised by the County Agricultural Society.

Jack Heywood and Ian Hepworth, two well-known farmers from Hampshire,
were invited to come up and judge the Competition. When the judges were shown
round the farm, I have to say, in all modesty, that the farm with its heavy crops
and healthy-looking livestock was looking well.

*   *   *   *

Two days after the judges had been round we received a phone call from Philip
Shepperd, the County NFU Secretary to let us know that we had been awarded
second prize in the County Farm Competition. As entries had come in from all
parts of the County and as there were twelve entries, Julie and I were in a
transport of delight.

"You're a clever old boy," Julie said to me.

"I think it was the lunch you gave the judges," I said.

"Could be," said Julie, "the apple pie was a bit special and both of the judges
had second helpings."

I went out to tell the men the good news, and that they and their wives were
invited to a little celebration in the back room of the Dog and Duck on the
following Friday evening. In his phone call Philip Shepperd had said that there
would be a 'farm walk' round the top two farms, in ten days time.

It is an extraordinary fact that farmers, when they have discovered a better way
of doing things or how to improve their profits, happily share their knowledge
with other farmers.

We somehow didn't feel that we were in competition with each other although
Julie had been heard to say, in her wisdom, that in the present tide of massive
increases of output and production, the greatest enemy of an efficient farmer was
another efficient farmer and there could be a lot of truth in that.

*   *   *   *

The winner of the Farm Competition was Frank Orton whose farm lay just to the north of the main road that runs from Ipswich to Bury. Frank's father, old J.J. Orton who had been something of a rough diamond, had left Frank just over a thousand acres in 1936 and during the War Frank had increased his holding to two thousand four hundred acres.

He had married his wife, Gladys, in 1941. She had been one of the Land Girls on the Orton farms during the War and now ran the farm office. They had three children and, although Frank had left the Village school where he had been something of a failure, at fourteen, he had been able to send his daughter, Christine, to Cheltenham Ladies College and his two sons to Millfield. The eldest son, Simon, had won his school colours at cricket and had been given a trial for Middlesex. Frank had told Simon that the easiest way to get a farm was to marry the only daughter of a wealthy farmer and advised Simon to keep his eyes open!

The Frank Orton farms were a very high quality, chalky clay loam and, in spite of receiving no college education, Frank had turned out to be the best farmer in the area. At the Home Farm he ran a magnificent herd of two hundred Pedigree British Fresians. The Glendale Herd was among the three top herds in the Country.

Over the years Frank had enjoyed considerable success with his cattle in the showring. However, he had a ruthless streak and when Quinton Weston, the millionaire owner of West Riding Farms in Yorkshire, won the Championship for the Best Cow at the Royal, three years running, Frank went up to George McClean, the head cowman of West Riding Farms, and asked him, quite blatantly, what salary he would require to come and work for him in Suffolk. Frank then proceeded to make him an offer that the man couldn't refuse. Two years later, with George McClean showing his cattle, Frank won two first prizes at The Royal, the Female Championship and the Lord Avondale Cup for the Best Group of Three.

I remember that when I told Julie that George McClean had gone to Frank, she said, "I don't think you would do a thing like that Albert, and pinch another man's herdsman."

"It goes on all the time," I said, "the head cowman may be responsible for a top pedigree herd worth over a million pounds and if he can get high milk records and can turn out animals that look good and win at the shows and sales, he's worth his weight in gold. He can put tens of thousands into the owners' pockets."

The annual sale of the Glendale British Friesians was a day not be missed by anyone who was anyone in the British Fresian world. A string of overseas buyers from New Zealand, Italy, the USA and Israel had shown great enthusiasm to purchase animals from the Glendale herd at very high prices. The bull, Glendale Nutcracker, out of Glendale Golden Girl 106th, a two thousand galloner with her first calf, had been exported to South Africa for £20,000.

*   *   *   *

This was the afternoon of the farm walk and Frank's yard and buildings were immaculate. Shrubs, rose bushes and bulbs had been planted in gardens round the farm buildings and, with a full time gardener throughout the Spring and Summer the farmstead was a blaze of colour. Frank knew everything about presentation. When a potential buyer came, Frank would ensure that his herdsmen all wore white coats, and when they led out the bull or the heifer or the cow, the animals were groomed and turned out to perfection. Frank would sometimes ask an astronomical price for one of his young bulls and the buyers, partly mesmerised by the slick presentation, would usually cough up.

Frank grew two hundred and eighty acres of potatoes, and he had built a large processing plant for washing and packing the crop. Over the years he had convinced his neighbouring farmers to allow him to process and pack their crop. Frank had always said, with a knowing smile, that there was more money to be made out of farmers than there was by farming.

Up on the higher ground, away from the frost pockets, Frank had ninety acres of apple orchards, mostly Cox's and Bramley's, and next to the apple orchards were sixty acres of strawberries for a 'Pick Your Own' enterprise. In addition, there were thirty acres of blackcurrants on contract to Ribena and ten acres of daffodils for bulbs. Every field was neat and clean and it was difficult to see a weed anywhere. He was indeed a perfectionist and I felt very honoured to be placed second to this magnificent farm with its superb management.

Frank came up and sat beside me in the trailer.

"Congratulations, Frank," I said, "I've never seen your farm look better."

"Well," said Frank, "I think that as I get older I make less mistakes than I used to and I've got some good men. In fact, I prefer to think that there are no bad men, only bad masters. I've got three foremen and they know what I want. I seldom give them orders, but sometimes when I want something done, I lay the thought in their minds and let them think of it themselves."

I knew that Frank paid above average wages but he provided his men with the right machinery and materials to do the job well and he insisted on a high standard of work. He allowed his tractor drivers to put in as much overtime as they wished during the planting and harvesting seasons. He was interested in getting the job done while the weather was right and he expected his staff to finish the planting and to have gathered in the harvest before any of his neighbours.

There is no doubt that Frank would have been a great success in the City or in industry.

"The trouble now is," said Frank, "the supermarkets have got us in their grip. They are slow payers and drop you like a brick if you don't measure up. Last year I dumped a hundred tons of carrots for stock feed because they were a few millimetres too long!"

CHAPTER THIRTY-FIVE

The Pest

It was early season, two years later. We were already collecting fertile eggs from the nestboxes of our outdoor mating pens and filling the incubators ready for the Spring rush. Our order book for chicks was already full from the beginning of February till early May. Helmet had sent in three pens of our pullets, the previous year, and they had won first and third prizes in the National Laying Trials. This had been a great boost to our trade and orders were coming in from all over the Country.

Suddenly, in the third week in February, the number of eggs collected dropped alarmingly. This was a warning that something was drastically wrong. Julie and I walked together round the acres of outdoor breeding pens. We noticed that some of the birds were looking decidedly mopey and there was a darkening of their combs and wattles. We opened the door of one of the hen houses, and then I heard that dreaded gasping, croaking cackle in the hens' throats and it confirmed my worst fears that our breeding flock, of which we were so proud and that we had steadily improved year by year, had been hit by an outbreak of the dreaded disease of Fowl Pest.

I rushed indoors and telephoned Dick Bell, the Ministry Poultry Officer, and within two hours the Ministry vets had confirmed our suspicions. We were informed that every bird on the farm would have to be destroyed.

Barley straw, soaked in disinfectant, was spread across the farm entrance and large warning signs, saying

'KEEP OUT – FOWL PEST'

were placed on the roadside.

Julie was in tears and Peter and Sally came over to see if they could help.

*   *   *   *

During the next two days, two vets from the Ministry, Helmet, Happy Tattersall and myself wrung the necks of five thousand and thirteen innocent hens, twelve hundred and twenty one point of lay pullets and four hundred and eighty magnificent breeding cockerels.

As this had been compulsory slaughter by Government order we received compensation, and prices were high. All the hens and pullets were paid for at two pounds each and the cockerels at three pounds each and after two months we received a cheque from the Ministry for twenty four thousand nine hundred and eight pounds. This was a princely sum of money for the slaughtered birds, but no money was available for our enormous consequential losses. We would not be back in full production for a least eighteen months and our day old chick trade, which had been going so well, would have to be rebuilt. It was a dreadful blow, and our losses would run into tens of thousands of pounds.

We were determined to keep on Helmet and our two poultry students, Audrey Drew and Buffy Snell, who had been with us for six years and who had received their National Diplomas from the Harper Adams Agricultural College. We would find them work cleaning and disinfecting every incubator, nestbox and slat and after two months we would be able to begin restocking the Poultry Unit.

The Fowl Pest had hit us at a particularly unfortunate time. Before the War one third of eggs consumed in Britain were imported. Now the Poultry Industry was racing towards greater home supplies and self-sufficiency and we didn't want to be left out of the opportunities to cash in on the great boom and expansion of British poultry production.

CHAPTER THIRTY-SIX

The Stick

"Fifty million, all dwelling on a small island, growing only enough food for only, shall we say, thirty millions ... is a spectacle of insecurity which history has not often seen before."

Sir Winston Churchill

"The farmers are getting plenty of stick from the urban community at the moment, they say that they are producing too much food and are getting too much subsidy." Stuart was talking.

We were over for dinner with Peter and Sally and the ladies had gone into the drawing room for coffee, and Jim, Stuart, Peter and I were still sitting round the dinner table with the port bottle.

"It is incredible to see farmers put in the doghouse for producing too much food," I said. "We have been urged by one government after another to maximise production and now it has suddenly been decided that there is too much food in Europe. We are the most efficient farmers in Europe and are victims of our own efficiency and now we are asked to pay the penalty. We farmers have now joined the ranks of the unloved along with solicitors, teachers and estate agents."

"You have to admit," said Jim, "that the farmers have been feather-bedded, and soon you will be like the American farmers and be paid to grow nothing."

"There isn't a country in the world that doesn't subsidise its agriculture," I said. "The Americans and Japanese and all the European countries support their farmers on a massive scale."

"What's the good of that?" said Jim, cutting the end off of his cigar, "and it is ridiculous having all this food over here while half the world is starving."

"I would agree with that," said Peter, "but if there were no subsidies the food would be much dearer for the housewife."

"That's a load of rubbish," said Stuart, "we can go out into the world markets and buy in cheap food from places like Africa, South America and New Zealand."

"Yes," I said, "and take the food from the mouths of the starving in the Third World. And what is more, I shouldn't want to be a New Zealand farmer at this moment. They are having a very rough deal with hundreds of farmers going bankrupt."

"There are some very strange things happening with food prices over here," I said. "In a pub, a baked potato with a bit of cheese sprinkled over it costs as much as the farmer gets for half a sack of potatoes? In fact, for another 50p you can buy, from the farmer, a whole sack of potatoes. During the last fifteen years the price of

168

a car has doubled, a tractor has trebled and a loaf of bread has trebled, and during this time the price of wheat has only risen by 5%. You might also think it odd that a pint of beer containing 98% water of unknown analysis costs four times as much as a pint of fresh milk of specified guaranteed analysis."

"And another thing you spoilt urbanites ought to know," said Peter, "is that fifteen years ago I could a buy a tractor by selling thirty of my bacon pigs, and now to buy an equivalent tractor I have to sell one hundred and forty bacon pigs."

"Another thing," said Jim, helping himself to another glass of port, "you are destroying the countryside."

"Well," I said, "you'd certainly think so if you listen to what the ramblers, the RSPB and the 'green' people say. To the public mind, the barn owl and the skylark enjoy much more esteem than the cereal farmer. Quite honestly, nearly all farmers are conservationists. We have to live in the countryside ourselves and we nearly all love trees and skylarks and robins."

Sally came in. "Have you lot finished putting the world to rights?" she said.

"Not really," I said, "Jim and Stuart are still unconvinced that farmers are a great asset to the Nation."

"Ah, well," said Sally, "you'd better come through or your coffee will be cold, and Peter bring in a couple of logs with you."

CHAPTER THIRTY-SEVEN
The Sheep

Our sheep enterprise consisted of five hundred, six and eight tooth, Scottish half-bred ewes. These North Country sheep were bred by using a Cheviot ram with its strong white face on a Border Leicester ewe.

Every year, Julie and I took two days off and attended the sheep sales at Penrith. We would buy in about two hundred shearlings a year to replace the broken mouth ewes that we were discarding. In October these shearlings were mated with our Eastern Counties black faced Suffolk Tups. The result of this three way cross was that we hoped each year, by careful shepherding and with the help of a few triplets, to rear nearly a thousand lambs from our five hundred ewes. To see five hundred ewes and a thousand lambs in a forty acre field by the roadside was a wonderful sight and we have seen the time in the late Spring and early Summer when, on a Sunday afternoon, there would be a dozen cars parked on the road by the sheep and the people were watching the lambs gambolling round their enclosure.

We were anxious, however, to increase the number of our lambs that we could fatten per acre. We had already studied the various types and strains of grasses for maximum yield throughout the fattening season. Certain strains of grasses from Denmark and the Plant Breeding Station at Aberystwyth were definitely superior to our common English grasses. Our seed mixtures blended in the strong early Italian rye grass, meadow fescues, Kent Indigenous rye grass, and from Suffolk, Kersey White clover.

*   *   *   *

Julie and I arranged to go down to Wales and see a nationally known, progressive sheep farmer by the name of David Lloyd-Jones. We knew that David was rotationally grazing his sheep and was getting a remarkable weight of fat lamb per acre. We phoned and asked David Lloyd-Jones if we could come down and see his sheep and we motored down one Sunday in May to Crickhowell.

After David had given us a very stiff whisky we went out to see his sheep. He mentioned two things which were known to most sheep farmers. The first was that the greatest enemy of a sheep is another sheep, and, secondly, that sheep should not hear the church bells twice in the same paddock. The problem was worms. Intestinal worms and parasites, according to David, were the main cause for lambs doing badly. If sheep remained for any length of time in the same paddock, the worms which passed through the sheep, just went round and round and the sheep would lose weight and then it became necessary to dose them with all sorts of deworming chemicals. This, according to David, was an expensive and unnecessary chore.

*   *   *   *

So we returned to Broadshots and we purchased hundreds of yards of sheep netting and hundreds of five foot chestnut stakes and split a fifty acre grass ley into five, ten acre paddocks. We lined the top of the wire netting with barbed wire and made the paddocks really sheep proof. Every five days the sheep were moved into a fresh paddock. The worms that had passed through the sheep would die after ten days of exposure to sun and weather.

During the next few months we had many visits from sheep farmers throughout East Anglia and Kent to look at the results of our rotationally grazing systems.

I was invited to be the main speaker at the National Sheep Breeders' Conference at the University Arms in Cambridge, where a scout from Anglia TV asked me if I would go up to Norwich, the next Sunday, to appear on their farming programme.

*   *   *   *

When I entered the Anglia Television building at Norwich the first person I saw was Greg Butterfield, who was a part-time reporter for the agricultural press. Greg was something of an expert on general farming matters and the higher politics of agriculture.

Greg said to me, "Albert, what are they paying you?"

I had considered, wrongly, that it was a great honour to be asked to appear on television, and I hadn't given a thought to being paid for it.

"Don't do it for less than thirty quid," he said. "They'll try to screw you down."

"I didn't have long to wait before Greg was proved to be right. A pretty, leggy, young woman approached me with an official form, while I was having coffee. The form indicated that I agreed to say my piece for twenty pounds. I was asked if I agreed to this and would I sign? I hadn't got the nerve to disagree.

We had a rehearsal in the morning for the live programme in the afternoon. All the tripe was ladled out to us 'new boys'. "Relax. Don't lose your temper. Don't scratch your nose and for Christ's sake, don't look at the cameras."

I don't remember too much about my interview but I found myself talking much more freely than I had anticipated. I remember the hot studio lights, the zooming cameras and the mike round my neck, and my amazement at how the presenter seemed to be learning, off by heart, all his words. I was grateful when he asked me a question about wintering sheep, and I hadn't got too ready an answer, how he was able to keep the interview rolling.

When I got home, Julie, who had watched the programme with Peter and Sally, said, "You were very good, darling. I expect you will become the John Cherrington of the Eastern Counties."

"Not much fear of that," I said, "I felt a bit of a clot up there, with all those bright people in Norwich."

CHAPTER THIRTY-EIGHT
The Show

The East Anglia Agricultural Show was held annually during the second week in June. It was the most important event in the Eastern Counties calendar. The Show, which was held on a Wednesday and Thursday, attracted crowds of over eighty thousand people.

The Show Secretary and Chief Executive was Jim Martin and he had been appointed just after the War. Jim was thirty six and was a man of considerable stature and discretion. Jim had been a half-Colonel in the 17th Regiment Royal Horse Artillery during the War, and as a Battery Commander had had a Japanese bullet through his hat when setting up an O.P. on the Chindwin in Burma. Jim had flown light aircraft before the War, and he had been on a course in Rhodesia flying Lysanders which were used by the artillery for O.P. spotting.

In December 1944 he was directing his Battery of 25 pounders from an aged Lysander when he was shot down by a Japenese Zero fighter. Fortunately, he was saved by his parachute but was taken prisoner, and was housed with countless other nationalities, including Chinese, in the notorious Rangoon jail.

When Jim took on his job as Show Chief Executive he dropped his rank. It was not considered a helpful policy to flaunt one's military or service rank in Agricultural circles after the War. Farmers and farmworkers, in the interests of food production, had been exempt from military service. So Jim was seldom referred to as 'Colonel' except by his regimental acquaintances.

On the question of rank, in agricultural circles, there had been the delicate matter of Rufus Dodd-Jones and Air Vice-Marshal Halbert Newton-Carver. Rufus had been a low grade bank clerk before the War and although he worked quite diligently in the bank, he was thoroughly spoilt by his doting mother and possessed a certain dull stupidity. On being conscripted in 1940 Rufus was drafted into the Army Pay Corps at a unit at Southwell in Nottinghamshire. Being a good Christian, he regularly attended Morning Prayer and the Holy Eucharist at the beautiful Southwell Cathedral, with its twin west towers. For dinner on Saturday nights, together with his immediate superior, Sargeant Hattersley, Rufus patronised the Saracen's Head Hotel, where King Charles I had given himself up to the Scots. After six months Rufus was promoted Corporal and occasionally knocked about with a short, fat ATS girl from Nottingham. Towards the end of his second year at Southwell he had an amazing bit of luck.

He was posted to a Pay Unit near Crediton in Devon where he found that the Colonel of the Unit was none other than his Uncle Jack who had been a bank manager in Exeter. From then on the army career of Rufus took off. He was recommended for a commission and by Christmas 1942 he was a fully-fledged

Lieutenant and he began to throw his weight about among the lower orders. The lower orders referred to him as 'The Pest' and found him irksome, arrogant and a pain in the neck. Rufus spent the next three years down in Devon. He ended up in 1945 with the rank of Captain. He had had a 'good war' and hadn't heard a bomb drop or a shot fired in anger. On demobilisation Rufus was given his old job back by his pre-war, caring employers in the High Street who were sensitive of their duty to returning War heroes as well as being compelled to reinstate previously employed personnel after military duty, by Government decree.

In 1947 Rufus was left a three hundred acre farm by a wealthy aunt. The farm was a high quality, boulder clay soil in West Suffolk. His aunt had also left him a fine herd of pedigree Hereford cattle. A pedigree herd of Hereford cattle invited considerable prestige, and Rufus became a paid up member of the internationally known, Hereford Cattle Society. To ingratiate himself to the Society and some of its senior and influential members he paid four thousand five hundred and fifty guineas for a bull from the famous Vern herd at the Show and Sale in Hereford. Rufus also ordered a thousand sheets of top quality Basildon Bond embossed note paper with the heading:-

'THE COPPERFIELD HERD OF PEDIGREE HEREFORD CATTLE'
The property of Captain Rufus Dodd-Jones.

and on the top right hand corner was an imposing picture of a stately, imperious-looking, white faced Hereford bull.

Rufus was determined to cut a bit of a dash and play a full part in the rural scene. He purchased a horse and hunted regularly in the Winter, and to curry favour with the Hunt, he invited them to hold a lawn meet at his substantial residence. Here, he and his wife, Poppy, dispensed to the mounted members of the Field and to a specially privileged section of the foot followers, fruit cake and cherry brandy.

Rufus also joined the Middlesham Branch of the Country Landowners Association where he had quite a lot to say. In fact, he appeared to have instant views on any subject. He was conscious of his rank in the Army Pay Corps and he let it be known that he wished to be referred to as 'Captain Dodd-Jones'.

It so happened that another member of the Middlesham Branch of the CLA was Air Vice-Marshal Halbert Newton Carver, 'Reggie' to his friends. The Air Vice-Marshal owned twelve acres of worn out, indiscriminate, thistle-choked grassland at the bottom of his six acre garden which he let out to a neighbour for spasmodic sheep grazing. His ownership of twelve acres entitled him to become a member of the CLA. The Air Vice-Marshal was not really 'up' in agriculture and land owning politics and from time to time made brief shallow comments which demonstrated a certain poverty of knowledge and comprehension of the technical and political aspects of land ownership.

There was, however, an historic occasion of the Middlesham Branch Annual General Meeting under the Chairmanship of Brigadier Hobbs, a substantial landowner.

The Meeting had gone well with full reports of the delegates on the doings of the Taxation Sub-Committee (The CLA was very hot on taxation), tenancy legislation, the Third London Airport and a short report on the dinner which had been arranged to meet M.Ps. and had been attended by the Chairman and Vice-Chairman in the House of Commons.

The matter arose of 'Bulls on Public Footpaths'. The Air Vice-Marshal, who was alleged to have a genial side to his character, but few people ever saw it, was strong on this subject. Needless to say, the Air Vice-Marshal had no cows or bulls and he proposed a resolution that it should be forbidden for any bull to run in a field where there was a public footpath.

Captain Rufus Dodd-Jones, however, did have cows and bulls. His old Hereford stock bull, with the official registered name of Copperfield Majestic 21st but which everyone else knew as 'Freddie', made friends with all the ramblers and walkers that crossed his paddock. So Captain Dodd-Jones violently opposed the resolution and proposed an amendment. The gist of the amendment was that although the bulls of dairy breeds such as Friesians, Ayrshires and the Channel Island breeds, which were notoriously untrustworthy, should be banned from the footpaths, there should be no objection to quiet old bulls of the beef breeds, such as the Hereford and Aberdeen Angus, roaming the ramblers' territory.

The Chairman, however, made a bit of a slip and put the resolution to the vote. Whereupon Rufus leapt to his feet and said that people appeared to have forgotten their Committee procedure, and he insisted that the Chairman should put his amendment to the vote before he took the resolution. Rufus was quite right, of course, but it was the fancy and provocative way that he said it that won him few friends. He was also casting unwarranted aspersions on the competence of the Chairman. His detracting admonition caused the few remaining hairs on the Air Vice-Marshal's head to bristle.

On the way out from the meeting, the Air Vice-Marshal caught hold of Rufus' coat sleeve and, knowing full well that Rufus had served in the Army pay Corps, said, "I didn't know you were in the Navy, Rufus."

"I wasn't," said Rufus, "I was in the Army."

"Good Lord," replied the Air Vice-Marshal, "and do you mean to say that you only reached the rank of Captain?"

Rufus, who was fired with social ambition, made a mental note that when he was elected President of the County CLA and eventually became Lord Lieutenant of the County, he would ensure that Newton Carver was omitted from the County hospitality lists.

*   *   *   *

Jim Martin conducted, regulated, directed and administered the East Anglia Show, together with three full time assistants and three or four extra staff during the pre-Show period.

The Agricultural Society offices, which resembled black and white pantomime palaces, were situated behind the Grand Ring and this indeed was a hallowed area. Not only were the Society offices in this special area of the showground but some fifty yards to the west there was the much venerated sanctity of the President's Enclosure which, on show days, was festooned with ferns and massed geraniums.

Orbiting around this inner sanctum, the inner circle of the Show displayed the collective consciousness of the County people.

Next door to the President's Enclosure was the Members' Luncheon Tent and the Judges' and Stewards' Marquee. Behind the Judges' and Stewards' Marquee was a rather magnificent 'loo' for the Lady Members. This tented edifice had a dozen flush toilets, with dressing-tables, wash basins and plenty of mirrors in the Powder Room. The two elected ladies on the Council had won golden opinions from the Lady Members for their sterling efforts at meetings of the Show Council, on behalf of the fairer sex.

Although Jim Martin ran the Show, there were, however, many other people who thought that they did. These included the Chairman of Council, the Honorary Director, the foreman of the Showground staff, the Chief Steward of Horses and the Chief Steward of the Grand Ring and in one memorable year, the highly-charged wife of the President. Many other worthy people considered that the success of the Show depended almost entirely on them. Among those of that persuasion were the Secretary of the Dog Show, the Secretary of the Poultry Show, the W.I. County Chairman, all the members of the Flower Show Committee and the lady organising the Arts and Crafts marquee.

There were others who were convinced that their duties and responsibilites were the most important within the confines of the Showground. Among those was the Chief Steward of Car Parks, the course builder for the jumping competitions, the local Vicar, who was in charge of the Church Stand and with some justification, Lucy, the girl in the office who checked the entries and pacified irate, complaining exhibitors who stormed into the office during the two days of the Show.

*   *   *   *

The chief big shot of the Show was the President, who was elected annually at the Council Annual General Meeting.

The President of the year's Show was Sir Julian Rhodes-Coxon. Sir Julian was an outstanding example of the great amateur county gentleman. He owned five thousand acres of farmland and woodland. The Home Farm of six hundred acres was in hand and farmed by Peter Stiles, his Farm Manager. The remainder was let to nine tenant farmers, all of whom extracted a good living from the land. The rents were all relatively modest and the farm buildings were kept in good repair.

Sir Julian had served in the Essex Yeomanry during the 1914–18 War, where he had been a Squadron Commander in the Cavalry. He had taken part in the great Cavalry charge at Monchy Le Preaux in April 1917 where he had been wounded.

The tenants were much afeared of what would happen when Sir Julian's nineteen year old nephew, Simon, who was now at the Royal Agricultural College at Cirencester, took over the management of the estates. There was talk of a substantial rise in rents and of eleven per cent being charged on improvements.

Sir Julian had that air of diffidence and aloofness that marked the high ranking gentleman. He was always referred to by his staff as 'The Major'. He was a recognised authority on the breeding of fox hounds and he showed hacks at Olympia. In his younger days he had been a useful cricketer and was a fearless hooker of the short ball. During one of his visits to India to see his sister, Vanessa, who had married the Bishop of Bombay, he had played for a British Embassy eleven, and had scored one hundred and four runs against the Bombay Police and the Public Works Department. After that match the Indian Chief of Police had remarked that Sir Julian had played "a very bloody good innings".

The Rhodes-Coxons lived in an enormous, ten bedroomed, house, full of valuable paintings and opulent furnishings.

Sir Julian had been High Sheriff of his County in 1951. During his period of office as High Sheriff he had led many money raising events for charity. He attended church as an example to the lower orders.

Lady Rhodes-Coxon was certainly no oil painting, and Alan Drew, one of the Grandstand stewards, had said that she had a face like an adjustable spanner. She had been born in India during the rule of the Raj, and the burning sun had left its mark on her complexion of faint crows' feet and dehydrated skin. However, Lady Rhodes-Coxon was a well-bred woman and she always dressed in the first flight of fashion. She had a strong tendency to hit the gin bottle and she had been known to berate the cook at dinner. When shopping in the local town, she would not hesitate to upbraid the young girl assistants in the hat shop and when the case was justified, would go along in person and make a complaint to the Village grocer.

*   *   *   *

So Sir Julian and his wife took their rightful place at the top of the intricate social strata of the local rural community.

As President of the Show, Sir Julian was expected to provide, out of his own pocket, lunch for about eighty dignitaries on both the first and second day, in the President's Pavilion. His caterers would lay on a hundred and twenty dainty teas each day in the marquee for invited guests. The President would be lucky if he could emerge from the honour and obligations of Office for less than five thousand pounds.

Lady Rhodes-Coxon agonised over the guest list. It was obligatory that certain dignitaries should be invited to lunch on the first day. These included the Lord Lieutenant, the Lord Bishop, the Chairman of the County Council, the corporate Mayors and their wives from Councils in the Show catchment area. There would also be around half a dozen Members of Parliament from the local constituencies. On this occasion the Rhodes-Coxons had invited Sir Henry Plumb, the President of the National Farmers' Union and also the French Minister of Agriculture.

Needless to say, many would feel snubbed and offended at not being invited to this quite modest junket and the President's wife would often lose sleep over these delicate problems of hurt feelings and protocol.

Lady Rhodes-Coxon, who was sensitive about her image, forced the rhythm of the County Set. She was uncomfortably seated on the horns of a private dilemma concerning the invitations to lunch at the Show as far as her own immeditate family was concerned. There was no problem with their elder daughter, Dominique. Dominique had married Nigel, the eldest son of General 'Bungay' Wainwright. Nigel was already a director of three successful property companies and had helped build Milton Keynes. He and Dominique lived in an impressive eight bedroomed, mock Georgian house, in Sunningdale. The house had a jacuzzi by the pool and three garages, presently occupied by a Silver Cloud Roller, a 3.2 Daimler for shopping and a brand new Land Rover for town and country. Nigel's Roller delivered him for lunch at Claridges once a week where he met his business clients and colleagues.

Dominique, who as a complete snob, looked well on a horse and was the apple of her mother's eye. She had appeared in a photograph in the November issue of *Harpers and Queen*, as Chairman of a Charity Ball for the homeless of Kensington. She was shown shaking hands with Mrs. Anthony Eden.

The younger Rhodes-Coxon daughter, Harriet, on the other hand had rebel blood in her and, at school, had interests other than botany and lacrosse. Harriet was now eighteen. A year earlier she had left Roedean rather hurriedly. When she should have been tucked up in bed in the dormitory, the duty Mistress had found Harriet in the back of a van belonging to Mickey Fox in a lay-by on the Brighton Road. Mickey was a sandle-wearing, pony-tailed drummer in the 'Hell of Dread' pop group.

After being expelled from Roedean, Harriet had taken herself up to London where, according to Dominique, she had 'shacked up' with Solly Cohen, a long haired, jobless 'ner do well' of the lentil and brown bread brigade. Solly wore very long ear-rings, had a ginger beard and wore steel-rimmed glasses. He was into heavy metal music and both Harriet and Solly were fervent devotees of the famous high beat rock band called 'The Sex Division.'

When invitations were being considered for the Show luncheons Harriet let it be known to her parents that in no way would she accept an invitation to the President's Lunch unless Solly was also invited. To invite Solly, who would undoubtedly turn up in jeans and a donkey jacket, to the President's luncheon was, in the eyes of Lady Rhodes-Coxon, a long way beyond the unthinkable. So Harriet, who her sister thought was four months pregnant, had to miss out on one of the great occasions in the County calendar. As an alternative experience Harriet would go off with Solly in an old Ford Transit van, with a supply of marijuana under the front seat, and some cans of ready made bean stew in the back. They would mix along with the pot-smoking flower children and other fringe people mucking along the hippy trail. They were destined to camp out at the 'Great Festival of Music' with music being provided by the bands of 'The Murderers', 'The Sex Rollers' and 'The Wild Barons', in a field in Dorset.

*   *   *   *

This year's show was going to be a very special show indeed as, on the first day, it was to be visited by The Queen Mother. When this became known it was plain to see that among the Landed Proprietors and those on the edge of the fashionable world, social ambitions shone with gathering brilliance.

Many months before, there had been long and detailed communications concerning the Royal visit with 'The Palace'. Her Majesty's chief equerry had been over a couple of times and met the Chairman of Council and the Chief Executive.

There had already been several changes of plan and in the early stages 'The Palace' had indicated that Her Majesty would be arriving in the Royal helicopter. This information galvanised the Council to enquire of 'The Palace' if it would be possible for the helicopter to land in the Grand Ring. To the considerable surprise of the Show officials 'The Palace' indicated that there appeared to be no reason why this should not be done. Preparations were then made for the reception of the Royal helicopter into the four acre Grand Ring. There were loud protests from the stewards of horses and ponies who appreciated that a low flying helicopter might cause considerable panic in the horse lines and in the livestock areas. This objection, however, was overruled by the Council who perceived the great publicity advantages of a soft landing of Her Majesty bang in the middle of the Showground and in front of a packed ringside and Grandstand.

Detailed plans were then made concerning the itinerary and the Queen Mother's programme. Paint was splashed around the main entrance and a gang of four workmen with wide paint brushes were tarting up the Grandstand.

Three days before the Show the Board of Trade announced that they forbade the landing of the helicopter in the Grand Ring in the interests of crowd safety. They said, however, that there would be no objection to the helicopter landing in one of the car parks. This, of course, messed up all the reception plans and a large letter H, in a forty foot circle, was painted on the grass in the West Car Park behind the cattle lines. This new arrangement entailed a new draft of the route and order of the Royal procession, and the Chairman of Council, the Honorary Director and the Chief Executive were beginning to show signs of wear.

Two days later, which was the day before the Show, the Press had their briefing as to the rearranged programme. This meeting with the Press had just been completed when there was a phone call from 'The Palace' to say that the Royal helicopter was unserviceable and Her Majesty would be travelling by train to Middlesham Station and would journey to the Showground by car. The Chief Constable would now have to secure the route from the Station to the Showground and arrange for the motorcycle Police escort. Schoolchildren would be given Union flags to wave on the route and the Middlesham Station Master would have to climb up into his attic for his top hat.

*   *   *   *

In the early hours of the morning of the Show the Chairman of Council, the Honorary Director, the Chief Executive and about five hundred others involved with running the Show listened with rapped attention to the 5.30am weather forecast. Among those who would be consumed with anxiety concerning the weather would be over a hundred and fifty stewards and double that number of exhibitors and stand holders. From his bed, in his house at Martlesham Heath, the treasurer Mike Shipman switched on his radio. He knew that the promise of fine weather, combined with a Royal visit, could increase the gate returns by over 20% and the profits by as much as 50%. Large numbers through the turnstiles could ensure that the Show would keep on a financial even keel for at least another year.

A sigh of measured relief must have embosomed those listeners to the area forecast for East Anglia. After a week of dry warm weather, a further few days of warm sunshine were predicted.

By 6.00am a few yawning stewards, who may have been lucky enough to have had a cup of tea and a bacon roll for breakfast, were already on the Showground. The stewards were attired, on Council orders, in dark suits, the County Show tie and bowler hats.

The Honorary Show Director was Peter Henderson. At this moment Peter was having an early breakfast with the Chief Cattle Steward in the Herdsmens' canteen. Those in the know knew that the best eggs and bacon breakfast on the Showground, during the early morning, was to be found in the Herdsmens' Club.

Many of the livestock herdsmen had been up since 4.30am, washing, feeding and rugging up their well-groomed exhibits. Cows in the dairy classes had to be milked out and the already clean coats of horses, pigs, sheep and cattle had to be washed again and shampooed, combed and blow dried.

By 6.00am the livestock pens had been mucked out and by 7.00am the animals had all been bedded down with clean straw and the dung removed from the Showground.

By 7.30am the sun had come out and began to dry up the slight summer mist. The acres of white tents and marquees sparkled in the shafts of sunshine and the many flags and banners topping the stands and marquees rippled in the gentle south wind.

"I reckon," said Walter Kibble, who was head pigman to Lord Scarfield, and who long before he had his own breakfast had been out exercising his eighteen month old Large White boar, "It's gonna be a scorcher."

"You're about roight there," said Ernie Gully, who was carrying half a bucket of water from the standpipe to his much fancied Landrace sow, "It's gonna be hot enough to stick yer tits togither."

*   *   *   *

It was 9.00am and all the judges, breakfasted, badged and bowler-hatted, had arrived from the local surrounding hotels. They displayed the red label on their car windscreens and were shepherded by the car park stewards to the VIP car park. The judges had first to report to the Secretary's office where they collected their judging books and their stewards, who would be at their beck and call all morning.

Most of the judges had brought their wives with them and while the judge got on with passing verdict on his classes, his wife, in her 'first day' hat, complimentary badge and shooting stick could go off and have an early look at the Women's Institute exhibits and the shopping arcade.

In many of the livestock classes the judges would have sorted out their prize winners by 11.30am, and the judge would join his wife for cocktails at the invitation of the Judge's Steward. This would be followed an hour later by a couple of gin and tonics, an excellent cold lunch of fruit cocktail, followed by cold salmon or beef or turkey, followed by strawberries and cream, cheese and coffee, all at the expense of the Show Society. The judge would also receive free passes to the special VIP enclosure in the Grandstand.

The costs of putting the judge and his wife up in a hotel with dinner and breakfast and the subsequent hospitality on the Showground were considerable and the Show Society hoped that the judge would not claim heavy travelling expenses.

It behoved the all important Judges' Selection Committee to select judges that were competent and those who had preferably judged at the Royal in recent years. Judges that had been invited to judge at the National Show at Stonely carried a certain glamour of respectability and most exhibitors would be happy to parade their animals before them.

It was now past 10 o'clock. The day was sunny and warm and there was just enough south westerly breeze to flutter the two Union Jacks on each end of the Grandstand. In front of the Royal Box the Royal Standard proudly rippled in the wind.

*   *   *   *

Everywhere the Show was coming to life. There was the low roar of tractors and the hum of driven machinery. Elevators, activated by small petrol engines, chattered as they reached for the sky. There were carts and waggons brightly painted in red and blue, and cultivators and ploughs and sets of harrows. The Poultry, Flower, Dog, Rabbit and Honey Shows were preparing for a busy day. Over in the heavy horse lines, harness was being burnished in the long corridors of loose boxes. In the W.I. tent all the traditional skills of the perfect housewife and mother were displayed.

The Band of the Grenadier Guards had marched into the Grand Ring under the command of Bandmaster Steven Foster, with his red face and waxed moustache. Bandmaster Foster now stood as straight as a gatepost just inside the main Grand Ring gates. On this glorious day the shafts of sunlight glistened on the guardsmens' polished cap badges and the edges of their trumpets. The crowd in the stands and round the Grand Ring were full of expectancy.

Near the centre of the Grand Ring the dignitaries who were to be presented to Her Majesty were lined up in order of seniority and importance. The men, in dark suits, were holding their bowler hats. Their ladies, in expensive outfits, were taking hold of the brim of their picture hats against the soft wind.

*   *   *   *

At 1102 hours precisely the Royal Car, black and gleaming, with the Royal Standard fluttering on the bonnet, glided slowly through the main, wide open, gates of the Grand Ring. In scarlet and bearskin, the Grenadier Guards struck up the National Anthem. Her Majesty had arrived dead on time and there was a feeling of some relief among the organisers that the Show was on its way.

After driving slowly once round the Ring to the enthusiastic cheers of the crowd, the Royal Car came to rest near the centre of the Ring, exactly over a small white painted cross which was precisely seven metres from the edge of the water jump, as planned.

The Lord Lieutenant, Colonel Richard Temple-Johnson, CB., OBE., TD., in full dress uniform then took charge and introduced Her Majesty to the Show President, Sir Julian Rhodes-Coxon and Lady Rhodes-Coxon. Lady Rhodes-Coxon was wearing a smart Harvey Nicholls pale blue outfit with matching hat. Sir Julian then introduced to Her Majesty the Chairman of the Show Council, Arnold Chamberlain, a very able two thousand acre farmer from East Harling and Thetford.

Arnold then introduced to Her Majesty, Peter and Sally. Peter, as Honorary Show Director, had spent long hours on the Showground during the year and had almost lived on the Showground during the past week.

Peter, in shaking hands with the Queen Mother, bowed from the neck and Sally bobbed her little curtsey.

"How are the entries, Mr. Henderson?"

"Cattle and livestock entries are slightly down on last year, Ma'am," said Peter, "but the number of horses and ponies increases every year."

"I expect you have seen very little of your husband during the last few days," smiled Her Majesty to Sally.

"He enjoys being Show Director," said Sally, "but it does seem to take over our lives during the last two weeks before the Show."

"I'm sure that he does it all very well," said the Queen Mother, as the reporters crowded round and the cameras flashed. She had the right words for everyone.

*   *   *   *

There was a slight problem over in the Horse Ring. Colonel Metcalf, an international judge, had just finished judging the Heavyweight Hunters and was pinning on the last of the rosettes. He had fixed the highly commended rosette on the headband of 'Merlin', a big boned bay shown and ridden by Mrs. Pierrepont-Nichols. The Colonel, bowler-hatted and in a long jacket and tight trousers and wearing heavy black framed glasses, was pleased with his selections and he was looking forward to a gin and tonic with his steward. At this moment Jim Martin and the Chief Steward of Horses hurried into the Ring.

Jim announced that the Hackney judge had had an accident on his way to the Showground and would not be arriving in time for the judging. Jim asked the Colonel if he would judge the Hackneys. The Colonel replied that he had never judged Hackneys in his life and knew very little about them, but he would do his best.

The Colonel stood in the middle of the Ring stroking his moustache, and eight high-stepping Hackneys entered and were driven round the Ring. The Colonel afterwards related that the Hackneys going round the Ring had made him feel quite dizzy and he was losing confidence in his ability to arrive at the right decisions.

Standing beside the Colonel in the middle of the Ring was Will Larkins the Ring Guard. Will, who was in a coachman's uniform, blew the post horn between classes. The Colonel said to Will, "What's the best horse here, Will?"

And Will, who attended several county shows as Ring Guard said, "Well, number five, the grey of Mrs. Dalton, usually wins it, Sir, and it usually beats Charlie Keaton's bay mare into second place." So the grey of Mrs Dalton was given first prize and Charlie Keaton's mare was placed second and this seemed to satisfy most of the Hackney fraternity.

*   *   *   *

Julie had had an unfortunate morning. She had been riding Lady Helena's show horse, Harvest Gold, in the Lightweight Hunter class. It was a big class of eighteen entries. Harvest Gold had been behaving impeccably, and had been pulled up in the line of the first three. The judge was Lady Honor Gibson, who had come up from Somerset to judge the class. Lady Gibson, who liked to ride as many of the horses as possible, mounted Harvest Gold and began to trot him round the Ring. She then pushed him into a sharpish canter on the Grandstand side of the Ring. When horse and rider were passing the Bandstand of the West Suffolk Yeomanry, the band, with rolling drums, struck up their regimental march. Harvest Gold, who was normally completely traffic proof, was surprised and frightened by this sudden loud outburst of trumpets and drums, shied to the left, gave a little buck and nearly ran into the water jump. Lady Gibson, who was a superb horsewoman, ended up on Harvest Gold's neck, but regained her seat amid much applause from the Ringside crowd. This had certainly put paid to any chances Harvest Gold had of appearing among the prizewinners.

When Julie took the horse back from the judge she apologised for Harvest Gold's behaviour. "Don't worry about that, Mrs. Cooper," said Lady Gibson, "The opening volley from the Band was rather overdone."

Standing beside me at the Grand Ring rail in the Members' Enclosure was a disappointed Lady Helena Carrington. Major Carrington sat in his wheelchair with the faithful Jim Butt in attendance. Julie had remounted Harvest Gold at the end of the line and the horse and rider were at peace with each other and Harvest Gold was standing as quiet as an old milk float pony.

Lady Helena said, "You know, Albert, those reins are like telephone wires and Harvest Gold is just telling Julie that he knows he's been naughty and is very sorry."

"So he jolly well should be," said Major Carrington, firmly.

*   *   *   *

Over in the Pig Lines the Queen Mother had a few words of conversation with Bob Moss. Bob was Head Pigman for Matthew Piddington, a wealthy City businessman, who had bought three farms in Cambridgeshire so that he could offset the farm losses against profits made in the City.

Bob Moss was probably the best pigman in the Country and could bring a pig into the Show Ring looking as if it had just come out of Elizabeth Arden's salon in the West End. Bob had won the championship in the Landrace classes with his boar, Markroyal Golden Dragon 31st, and had then gone on to win the Championship of All Breeds.

When the Queen Mother and her entourage had gone, Bob was surrounded by members of the Press who had been following the Queen Mother around the Show. With notebooks at the ready they enquired what the Queen Mother had said to Bob. Bob, who was sixty four years old and had been showing pigs since he had left school and was full of country cunning, said, "Her Majesty said to me 'I like your pig, Bob, but I don't think that it is as good as the sow you had at the Bath and West Show three years ago'." Bob told all this with tongue in cheek and a straight face and some of the more unsophisticated of the junior reporters were very puzzled and didn't know whether to believe him or not.

*   *   *   *

Sitting on a bale of straw in front of the Pig Stewards hut were two smallholder pig farmers, Dick Corby and 'Spiky' Halfhide. Dick owned twelve sows and Spiky had fourteen. They were old friends and were discussing the pig trade over a pint of beer. There was much cogitation on market prices and Spiky had said "the proice of pigs was 'rose' lars week'." Dick had just sent an eight year old Large White sow to Bury Market. Spiky, who had seen this old sow about for years when he had been over at Dick's, said, "What yew git shot on she then fer, Dick?"

"Well," said Dick, wiping his mouth, "Toime before last when she farrered she only had one and last toime she farrered she dint hev none at all so Oi bloody well got rid on her."

"Cor, if she dunt hev no pigs when she farrered yew dun roight. Yew could't roightly keep her arter that. How did she come owt on weight at the Market?" enquired Spiky, blowing the crown off his beer.

"Well," said Dick, "They put the owd sow on the scales and Oi hev ta say it weighed more'n Oi thought it would," and then after pause he pondered, rubbed his head and said, "Oi thought it would. Oi thought it would."

*   *   *   *

The main Grand Ring attraction was the famous musical drive of the King's Troop Royal Horse Artillery. The King's Troop R.H.A., with its forty horses and six guns is stationed at St. John's Wood in London. The duties of the Troop include the firing of the Royal Salutes in Hyde Park on Royal Anniversaries and State Occasions.

The full Troop arrived in vast horse boxes, buses and trailers during the afternoon before the Show. Two enormous marquees had been erected for the horses and soldiers. Hay, straw and water had been laid on for the horses. Hotel accommodation had been booked for the Officers.

I had been asked to liaise with their Commanding Officer, Major W.R. Bollingbroke, R.H.A. and he invited me to come to the Troop's rehearsal at six o'clock that evening. The six teams of horses and guns were lined up outside the main Grand Ring gates and Major Bollingbroke said, "Come with me, we will stand in the middle of the Ring." He went on to say, "Stand by me, keep perfectly still and you will be all right."

The horses and gun teams trotted, cantered and galloped all around us. The Musical Drive culminated in an exciting scissors movement at a furious gallop with alternate teams crossing in the centre of the arena. I can tell you this, that during the scissors movement at the gallop, the wheel of a gun carriage brushed my back. "That one was a little close," said the Commanding Officer, with a smile.

When I told Julie that night she was furious and said, "You men will try and show off. There was no need for you two to be in the middle of the Grand Ring at all. The Germans spent five years trying to kill you and now you are doing your best to get yourself killed by so called 'friendly' troops in the middle of the Showground. You boys must try and grow up."

V. Kneale

*   *   *   *

At 12.35 precisely the Royal Party entered their respective cars and drove to the Royal Pavilion for lunch. The Queen Mother was flanked by the Lord Lieutenant and the Show President and grace was said by the Lord Bishop. The excellent lunch was provided by two young caterers, Michael and Prudence Keeble, who had built up a thriving catering business in the Eastern Counties.

Down at the far corner of the luncheon tent the recently elected Mayor of Sutton Shields polished his tumbler, knife and fork with his napkin. "George," hissed his wife, "don't do that. You're not in the Mayor's parlour now and don't put your elbow in the butter."

*   *   *   *

Ray Spalding, the Chief Steward of the Grand Ring, was furious. The Grand Ring programme was running over half an hour late.

"What's the problem, Ray?" I said.

"It's the bloody course builder," he said, "he is supposed to know all about the horses that are entered and to set the jumps at a height where only three or four have clear rounds and we've had eleven clear rounds already. That means eleven jump offs. We'll be here all the bloody afternoon."

Eventually, however, the heavily sponsored Jumping Competition was completed and the arena party, consisting of ten sturdy members of the Middlesham Army Cadet Force, were dismantling the jumps and clearing the Ring. That morning Peter Waldegrave, Chief Steward of Cattle, was sorting out the silver cups to be placed on the green baize-covered table in front of the President's Box on the edge of the Grand Ring. In due course Her Majesty would be presenting the cups to the worthy winners of the Cattle Championships.

"Here Alan," said Peter to Alan Drew, who was Grandstand Steward, "do you know what it says on this silver cup?"

"What's that?" enquired Alan.

"It says," said Peter, "that 'This cup is awarded to the cow with the best udder' and underneath is inscribed 'In memory of my wife'."

"Good Lord," said Peter. "That is a compliment indeed. I doubt whether Miss Simmons will receive that sort of accolade."

Miss Simmons was the rather prim and proper fifty year old manageress in the Show Office. She had no sense of humour, a tight mouth and was rather flat chested.

*   *   *   *

The led cattle were marshalled in Indian file through the crowds and began to enter the Grand Ring for the Cattle Parade.

"Hey up, there. Watch yer backs."

The crowd parted quickly. Hereford bulls filed into the Ring like council aldermen. A young Ayrshire heifer was playing up and was backing away from her young and nervous stockman. "Now then, stop acting up."

There followed six shaggy Galloways and some big boned Charolais.

Tom Corbett and Willie Hall, two shrewd and canny Hereford cattle men, were leaning on the white painted ringside rails as three classes of Charolais plodded by in noble procession.

"Useless creatures," said Tom, "too much bone."

"Got to have bone," said Willie, "to hang the bloody meat on."

"First of all," said Tom, "they told us that they wanted small joints for the butchers. Now they are saying that we Hereford and Aberdeen Angus breeders are breeding our beef cattle too small."

Many English cattlemen were worried that in a few years time the Charolais would dominate the British beef market and they endeavoured to highlight the breed's blemishes and imperfections.

"I used Charolais A.I. on one of my cows last year," said Tom, "The calf had such a big head that it took the Vet and three of us nearly three hours to calve her down."

Tom and Willie were joined by Dennis Wake, a well-known breeder and exhibitor of Shire Horses. "Afternoon, Dennis," said Tom, "how did you get on this morning?"

"First for the stallion and second for the brood mare in a class of fifteen."

"The mare done well for you then," said Tom.

"Yes," said Dennis, "considering the big three brewers were there."

The commentator of the Grand Ring announced the main attraction of the display by the King's Troop R.H.A. "We'd better go and give them owd soldiers a look," said Willie.

"They've cawst the sponsor ten thousand quid, so we'd better see if they are wuth it," said Tom.

At 2.45pm Her Majesty re-entered the Royal Range Rover and returned to the Grand Ring where she was invited to present the Cattle Championship award and to watch the hunter parade and present the Hunter Championship trophy. After this Her Majesty returned to the Royal Box and watched the parade of the Mid-Eastern fox hounds. The three Royal cars, with police escort, then entered the Grand Ring and took Her Majesty back to Stansted Airport. Before she left the Queen Mother told Peter Henderson that she had thoroughly enjoyed her day and those that had been in her company thought that she really had.

Back in the Show office Jim Martin was checking the gate returns and said, "Forty one thousand, four hundred and one. That's two thousand up on last year, I must tell the President."

$$* \qquad * \qquad * \qquad *$$

It had been a day of hot sunshine and seven thousand gallons of beer had been drunk. The county gentlemen, in dark suits, and their wives in expensive summer dresses and hats had bathed in the tingle and medium of the Royal Visit. The Show's finances and future was secure for another year. The High Sheriff, the Mayor and the Lord Bishop were driven back to their homes in their chauffer driven cars. The Members of Parliament and their wives returned to their constituencies. The troopers of the King's Troop Royal Horse Artillery watered their Irish-bred horses under the watchful eye of their Sergeant Major.

Over in the pig lines Bob Moss, whose champion Landrace boar had gone on to win Best of Breed, had ended up with two championships, two firsts, a third and a highly commended. Bob had already had five or six pints in the stockmen's canteen and he climbed into the back of his well-appointed pig lorry, got out his sleeping bag and knew that the weeks and months of planning his show successes had been really worthwhile and it would be true to say that Bob and men like him were the salt of the earth.

CHAPTER THIRTY-NINE
The Closing Years

It was Easter Sunday and Julie and I were walking the half mile or so home from Church. It had been Easter Communion, and we were accompanied by our two Godchildren, Jonathan and Alison. They had both been confirmed at school. They were two bright young people and Jonathan was in his second year, reading Law at University College Oxford, and Alison had just been given a place at Edinburgh.

Peter and Sally had agonised over their childrens' future. Jonathan had already done a short farming course at Writtle College and he was determined to be a farmer. After University he would probably do the mandatory year travelling round the world with a backpack, and like many mothers Sally was very concerned that he might fall for an Australian or a New Zealand girl and be persuaded to stay out there.

Alison, who was nearly seventeen, was good-looking like her mother with fair hair and blue eyes and she had joined the 'under thirties' section of the Farmers' Club. Here she had met Roger Woodward, whose father owned at least six farms in Hampshire, and they had fallen for each other hook, line and sinker, and all that Peter and Sally could do was to await developments.

Jonathan and Alison had no inhibitions about calling us 'Uncle and Auntie' and today they had invited us out to a Sunday lunch at the White Hart because they said 'we had been so good to them'.

When Jonathan and Alison dropped us off at Broadshots I picked up a basket of logs and we lit the fire. Julie brought in a pot of tea and set it on the small gate-legged table by the log box. Julie said, "It was lovely to see those two young people so self-assured and so helpful and polite."

"I saw Jonathan take your arm and help you down the steps of the White Hart," I said.

"That wasn't absolutely necessary," said Julie, smiling, "and it is obvious that Alison thinks you're the cat's whiskers."

*   *   *   *

The years rolled by with a strange swiftness. The Second World War, which had claimed the hardest years of my life and where I had witnessed human weakness and human strength, was now receding into distant memory. The piece of shrapnel lodged in my thigh since Alamein had lately been troublesome. There had been umpteen X-rays. "Too near the artery to operate," they had said. But it had now settled down.

Julie and I had shared more than half our life together. In this small pocket of time we had an inner contentment and these were moments of great happiness.

We never ceased to marvel at the running of the seasons. The seemingly near suspension of life and sound in the dormancy and the cold silence of Winter followed in due time by the chaos of sensations while the blood throbs like smoke in the resurgent life in the Spring.

It was mid-Winter and Julie and I stood in front of the roaring fire. There was a hard freeze and great sheets of ice were locking the reeds on the pond. As I peered through the curtains I could see outside the black boarded end of the great tithe barn and against the dark background were sheets of snow, relentlessly driven by a biting wind.

There was a knock at the back door. It was Dudley to say that there was no electricity in the farrowing house and the infra-red lamps that heated the piglets had been out for two hours. Julie tried to phone the Electricity Company but the lines were dead. I pulled on my heavy waxed coat, cap and thick boots and, carrying a large torch, went with Dudley up to the farrowing house. There was a raw sting in the air and stars pierced through the cold.

When I pushed open the outside lobby door of the farrowing house we found that Dudley's wife, Helen, in padded coat and wooly hat, was there and also Happy Tattersall. Happy was now semi-retired and just worked half a day doing odd jobs. He had come up to see if he could help. He had already started up a tractor and towed up the petrol-driven space heater from the workshop. The space heater was now pouring heat into the well insulated farrowing house and the piglets would be all right.

At 2.00am Reg Daley, our local electrician, arrived in his Land Rover and by half past the whole farm had light and heat.

As I walked back to the house the snowfall had stopped and a bright halo was forming round the moon. Happy, in his box cloth leggings and his green trilby hat, came down for a cup of coffee.

I had looked in, on the way back to the house, at the hatchery. The great incubators were still running. Within the last ten minutes Helmet had switched off the auxiliary generators and had just gone home.

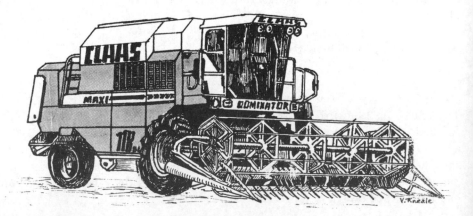

In this cold snap, with the puddles frozen bone hard in the bitter cold of a Winter's night, there were many birds and animals dependant on our energy and our competence and our close attention.

Julie made bacon sandwiches and coffee as the wind played tunes through the keyhole of the dairy door.

When Happy had gone and Dudley and Helen had returned to their cottage, I said, "You know Julie, we are very lucky to have staff that will take it upon themselves to turn out on a night like this."

"Yes," said Julie, catching me by the arm, "and they are lucky to have you."